Clyde Shipbuilding: *from old photographs*

1 *(Overleaf)* The *City of Paris* under construction at Clydebank in 1887, with frames and deck beams in position.
Riveting of the tank top is in progress.

CLYDE SHIPBUILDING

from old photographs

Introduction and commentaries by

JOHN R HUME

and

MICHAEL S MOSS

B.T. BATSFORD LTD

LONDON AND SYDNEY

To Robert Courtney Smith

'The teachers of youth are very right; of more
moment to Glasgow than her other industries, her
college, her cathedral, is the building of her ships'

James Hamilton Muir, *Glasgow in 1901*

First published 1975
Text © John R Hume and Michael S Moss 1975
ISBN 0 7134 2913 5
Filmset by Tradespools Ltd, Frome, Somerset
Printed in Great Britain by
The Anchor Press, Tiptree, Essex
for the publishers B.T.Batsford Limited
4 Fitzhardinge Street, London W1H 0AH
and 23 Cross Street, Brookvale, N.S.W. 2100, Australia

PREFACE

The impact of photography on Victorian Society was as great in industry as in the home. The same impulse that made parents have their children photographed during their childhood led industrialists to have their products photographed at various stages of construction and when complete. Despite the use of industrial photographs as a management tool, to record details and the advance of work on a contract, and for use as advertisement, the overriding consideration appears to have been to record with pride the achievements of the firm. In the last three years several remarkable collections of such photographs, dating back in some cases to the 1880s, have been discovered in the west of Scotland, largely as a result of the work of the Western Survey of the National Register of Archives (Scotland). These collections cover the whole range of west-of-Scotland heavy engineering from shipbuilding through locomotive building, stationary steam engine building, sugar machinery manufacturing, to constructional engineering, for a period when in these markets the west of Scotland dominated world trade.

The present book is confined in the main to shipbuilding prior to 1914. This date excludes many of the best-known Clyde-built ships such as the *Queen Mary*, and *Queen Elizabeth*; but such is the wealth of the collections of shipbuilding photographs that 1914 was chosen as a convenient break. The quality of the photographs illustrates the skill of the photographers, who were, in the small yards, amateur members of the workforce. Although these prints often lack the human drama of the more familiar genre of old photographs, they capture scenes and an atmosphere which were often more transient than those in the market place or on the vicarage lawn. Until the advent of photography there was no way of recording accurately ships that had been built only a few years previously, or even to record what a ship under construction had looked like on the stocks. As with all old photographs, these add a valuable dimension to our historical imagination and perspective, conveying at a glance what a Clyde shipyard was like in the Victorian and Edwardian period and illustrating the development, throughout the period, of shipbuilding and marine technology.

ACKNOWLEDGEMENTS

The authors wish to thank all those who, during the compilation of this book, and in their work for the Western Survey, helped in the location of photographs and other records of historical interest, and patiently answered innumerable questions. In particular they would like to mention: W. Adair, Lithgows Ltd; A. S. E. Browning, Glasgow Museums; Richard F. Dell, Glasgow City Archivist; J. Devine, William Beardmore & Co. Ltd; Dr J. Brown, formerly of John Brown Shipbuilding and Engineering Co. Ltd; T. R. Evans, Alexander Stephen & Sons Ltd; H. R. Gibbs, formerly of Barclay, Curle & Co. Ltd; J. G. Inglis; W. Lind; Sir William Lithgow, Bt; D. Lyon, National Maritime Museum; Stanley Mills, W. Ralston Ltd; T. Savage, Scotts Shipbuilding and Engineering Co. Ltd; G. A. K. Simpson, Royal Northern Yacht Club; A. Slaven, University of Glasgow; J. E. K. Smith, Upper Clyde Shipbuilders Ltd, Clydebank Division; R. C. Smith, Chairman of the Business Archives Council (Scotland) and Liquidator of Upper Clyde Shipbuilders Ltd; E. Souchette, formerly of Barclay, Curle & Co. Ltd; T. Wallace, Connell & Co. Ltd; and the late David Wilson-Reid, archivist, University of Glasgow.

Finally, the authors are greatly indebted to: David Vaisey of the Bodleian Library for suggesting the book; B. J. Reeves and D. Maclean for printing photographs; to Professor G. Melvyn Howe, Department of Geography, University of Strathclyde, and Professor T. Neville George, Department of Geology, University of Glasgow, for the use of photographic services; Lynne Bailie for reading the manuscript; and Lynda Kelly, Carolyn MacLean and Marion Merrifield for typing the (often illegible) manuscript.

The authors would like to thank the following firms and institutions for permission to reproduce photographs:

Anchor Line Ltd, no. 120
T. & R. Annan & Sons Ltd, no. 3
William Beardmore & Co. Ltd, nos. 39, 66, 101
Clarke Chapman – John Thompson Co. Ltd, Sir
  William Arrol Division, no. 42
Charles Connell & Co., nos. 59, 82, 91
Glasgow Museums of Technology Department, no. 4
Mr J. Inglis, no. 72
Keeper of the Records of Scotland, *Fairfield
  Collection*, nos. 9, 12, 17, 20, 22, 24, 26, 45, 57,
  58, 83, 88, 107, 111, 113, 115. *Clydebank
  Collection*, nos. 1, 5, 6, 8, 10, 11, 14, 16, 27, 29,
  31, 34, 36, 44, 46, 47, 48, 50, 56, 60 63, 64, 67,
  69, 70, 71, 73, 74, 75, 76, 78, 79, 84, 87, 90, 93,
  94, 95, 96, 97, 100, 102, 103, 106, 109, 110, 119;

Lobnitz Collection, nos. 23, 32, 35, 99, 104, 105,
  108.
Lithgow (1969) Ltd, nos. 2, 13, 15, 18, 25, 41, 52,
  62, 98, 114, 122.
Denny Collection, the National Maritime Museum,
  nos. 37, 38, 40, 51, 53, 65, 77, 80, 89, 121.
W. Ralston Ltd, nos. 52, 120.
Royal Northern Yacht Club, nos. 19, 21.
Scotts Shipbuilding and Engineering Co. Ltd, nos.
  28, 33, 43, 49, 54, 61, 68, 78, 81, 86, 92, 118.
Alexander Stephen & Sons, Linthouse, nos. 30, 85,
  112, 116, 117.
The Court, The University of Glasgow, Sir John
  Biles Collection, the University Archives, nos. 7,
  55.

CONTENTS

2 The steel, four-masted barque *Bermuda*, built by Russell and Company of Port Glasgow in 1893. This type of vessel was built in quantity on the Clyde, as it could compete with steam on longer voyages until the turn of the century. The *Bermuda* reached a speed of 14 knots, 'with a fresh quartering wind', and was equipped with labour saving devices and water ballast tanks with a steam pump.

AN HISTORICAL NOTE

From the early 18th century some small wooden fishing and coastal craft were built on the lower Clyde at Greenock and Port Glasgow. Scotts Shipbuilding and Engineering Company of Greenock, founded in 1711 as specialists in 'herring buses', is the only firm to survive from this period. During the century Greenock became the centre of ship-building on the Clyde, building, in 1776, 18 vessels of up to 97 tons. At that time American shipyards supplied the bulk of British trading vessels, but after the outbreak of the American War of Independence competition from British builders grew and the American share of the market decreased. However, only with the development of Scottish trade with the West Indies, which provided a new market for sizeable vessels built in Scotland, did Clyde shipbuilders reap any benefits, as there was a reluctance on the part of English owners to order from Scotland. In 1806 Scotts built the *Granada*, of 650 tons, and the *John Campbell*, of 446 tons, for this trade. By the beginning of the 19th century new shipbuilding centres had developed, especially at Port Glasgow and Dumbarton.

A major innovation with wide-ranging implications for Clyde Shipbuilders was the construction, in 1812, of the first commercially successful steam boat, the *Comet*, designed by Henry Bell of Helensburgh, built by John Wood and Company of Port Glasgow, and engined by John Robertson of Glasgow. The established yards were quick to adopt this new technology. Fifes of Fairlie, previously fishing boat specialists, built the hull for the PS *Industry* in 1814 exclusively for goods traffic between Glasgow and Greenock. Within a few years of the *Comet*'s success many steam boats had been built on the Clyde for estuarial navigation, including the first steam boat on the Thames, the *Margery* built by William Denny of Dumbarton. By 1818 32 steamers were in operation on the Clyde. Early steamers were used exclusively for short routes, where they could compete effectively with sailing vessels and the large coal consumption of the engines was not a serious disadvantage.

Despite the increases in the size and power of steam boats prior to 1818 little progress was made in designing hull forms for steam propulsion and improving the efficiency of the engines. The *Rob Roy*, which inaugurated the steam service between Greenock and Belfast and later between Dover and Calais, was built in 1818 by William Denny of Dumbarton. The hull design by David Napier resulted from some of the first model experiments to be carried out. David Napier and his cousin, Robert, soon came to dominate marine engineering in the West of Scotland. Robert Napier, while lacking his cousin's engineering genius, made up for this in business acumen, especially in his insistence on quality and reliability. Napier outlined his philosophy in a letter to Samuel

Cunard, dated 25 March 1839, discussing the engines for the first four vessels for The British and North American Royal Mail Company:

'I cannot and will not admit of anything being done or introduced into these engines but what I am satisfied with is sound and good . . . Every solid and known improvement that I am acquainted with shall be adopted by me, but no patent plans'.

This insistence by Napier on high standards was important, as, although Tod and MacGregor had built the Clyde's first iron shipyard at Springfield in 1835, the quality of Clyde-built iron hulls was often inferior to those built on the Thames and at Bristol. In the introduction to a short history and description of the firm of J. & G. Thomson, later John Brown and Company, published in 1896, the superiority of the Thames is acknowledged: 'At that time (1846) the Thames held first place in shipbuilding, if not also in engineering'. Until 1843 Robert Napier had most of his wooden hulls built by John Wood of Port Glasgow; but in 1841 he bought land in Govan for a shipyard, launching his first iron-hulled ship, the *Vanguard*, in 1843. The combination, in one enterprise, of iron shipbuilding and marine engineering proved successful and resulted in many of Napier's senior employees founding their own works and yards, notably James and George Thomson in 1846, and John Elder, in 1852.

Although steam ships at first were designed primarily for estuarial and cross-channel ferry services, it was not long before owners began to consider their introduction on trans-Atlantic routes. By 1833 Robert Napier had given serious thought to this subject and had expressed the desiderata for a successful trans-Atlantic steam ship company in a letter to Patrick Wallace, dated 3 April 1833:

'If your friends are in earnest about entering upon these speculations, they should make up their minds to meet with strong opposition and other difficulties for a short time. But, if they enter upon it with a determination to meet opposition and difficulties and to overcome them, then I have not the smallest doubt in my mind, but that in a short time it will be one of the best and most lucrative businesses in the country, provided always that the company set out right at first by having first class vessels fully suited for the trade in every department. I am aware that in getting up the first of these vessels, great care and attention will be necessary to gain the different objects in view, and in doing this, an extra expense may be incurred, but which may be avoided in all the other vessels. If the practical difficulties etc. are fairly surmounted in the first vessels – and which I have no doubt but they may – the first cost and the sailing expenses of the first two vessels ought not so much to be taken into account. In fact, I consider it as nothing compared with having them so efficient as to set any opposition at defiance and to give entire confidence to the public in all their arrangements and appointments, cost what it may at first, for upon this depends entirely the success, nay, the very existence of the company'.

The first steam crossing of the Atlantic was made by the *Sirius*, built in Leith, and engined by Thomas Wingate of Glasgow, in 1840. Robert Napier's firm had engined the

British Queen in 1839, a challenger for this distinction. It was, however, in the formation of Samuel Cunard's British and North American Royal Mail Steam Packet Company in 1840 that Napier was to find scope for his ideas. He recommended the use of larger and more powerful ships than Cunard originally intended, added a fourth ship to the projected order, and helped to raise capital on the Glasgow market. His direct involvement with the company was limited to engine building, and to the design of the hulls, which were built until 1856 by the firms of Wood and Steele on the lower Clyde. However, in that year the *Persia*, the first iron-hulled Cunarder, and the fastest vessel of the day, was completed at Napier's own yard. Other Cunarders built by Napier were the *Scotia* (1862), the most powerful steam paddler ever built, with a top speed of $14\frac{1}{2}$ knots, and the *China*, the first screw steamer built for Cunard. The success of this innovation in the *China* resulted in the abandonment of paddle-propulsion by the Company. From 1865, for the next 20 years, J. & G. Thomson, later John Browns, built most Cunard vessels, including, in 1870, the *Abyssinia* and *Algeria*, the last simple engined steamers for any Atlantic company. Thomsons, like Robert Napier, had a special relationship with Cunard, as their brother, Robert, was the firm's marine superintendent.

Cunard was not the only transAtlantic shipping company to buy vessels from Clyde yards. The Inman line's first vessel, the epoch-making *City of Glasgow*, was built by Tod and MacGregor in 1850. In the three years from 1856 the Allan, Anchor, Hamburg-America, Galway and Norddeutscher Lloyd lines were formed and all went to the Clyde for their first vessels. The principal exception was the White Star Line which, from the first, ordered its ships from Harland and Wolff in Belfast, although the Clyde can claim some credit for that firm's expertise as Harland had been trained by Thomsons. With the appearance of so many new companies the Cunard's monopoly was broken. Writing in 1896, Henry Fry commented that the firm, 'seemed to have fallen into the evils inherent in all monopolies. For thirty years they never altered the saloons, the state rooms, the bill of fare, the meal hours, or any of the details, they had no bath or smoking rooms, no piano, and only an apology for a lady's cabin. Even the type and form of the original "menu" were preserved'. The *Abyssinia* and *Algeria* built for Cunard by Thomsons in 1870 had proved markedly inferior to the contemporary Inman and White Star liners. Only the disastrous loss of the White Star *Atlantic* off Halifax in 1873 prevented Cunard from being totally eclipsed.

From 1870 onwards competition was fierce, each company ordering faster and better equipped vessels. In 1875, the Inman line ordered the largest Atlantic liner to date, the *City of Berlin*, from Cairds of Greenock. This ship was to become, in 1879, the first trans-Atlantic vessel with electric lighting; unfortunately her high fuel consumption of 120 tons per day, as compared with the White Star *Britannic*'s 80, made her uneconomical. The challenge was soon taken up by Cunard, who ordered the *Gallia* and *Serbia* from Thomsons in 1879-1881, and the *Umbria* and the *Etruria* from John Elder and Company (later the Fairfield Shipbuilding and Engineering Company) in 1884. Of the *Umbria* and *Etruria* Henry Fry was to write, in 1896, that 'their power and speed were unprecedented

11

and for a time they were the queens of the Atlantic'. These ships, the last single-screwed, main-line, trans-Atlantic vessels, gave Cunard a brief lead over its competitors and marked the beginning of a period of intense rivalry between the larger yards of Harland and Wolff, in Belfast, and the two Clyde yards of J. & G. Thomson and John Elder and Company. Because of the large capital requirements and the extensive plant and equipment required to build first-class Atlantic liners, the smaller shipyards were unable to compete in this market.

In 1877, the Inman Line, now under the control of American shareholders, decided to 'eclipse everything afloat' and ordered the *City of Paris* and the *City of New York* from Thomsons. These vessels were to be not only the fastest vessels on the American run, but were also to provide 'the comforts of home, with the richest luxuries of hotel life'. The photographs of the interiors of these ships certainly prove that Thomsons did justice to these aspirations. The *City of Paris* and *City of New York* went into service in 1888 and 1889 respectively, at the same time as the Belfast-built *Teutonic* and *Majestic* of the White Star Line. Competition was intense, all four vessels constantly clipping minutes off each other's records. Their glory, however, was to be short-lived, for in 1893, John Elder and Company, now Fairfield Shipbuilding and Engineering Company, built the *Campania* and *Lucania* for Cunard. In 1896 these vessels were described as 'the finest and fastest in the world' making regular 22 knot crossings. Henry Fry wrote of these vessels in 1896: 'The accommodations for passengers are sumptuous . . . the dining saloon is a vast, lofty apartment near the middle of the ship 100 feet long, 62 feet broad and 10 feet high, capable of seating 430 passengers in revolving chairs. The decorations are highly artistic: the ceiling is panelled in white and gold; the sides in Spanish mahogany and the upholstering is in a dark, rich red, figured frieze velvet, with curtains to match'. He sums up his description: 'What a monument to the skill of British shipbuilders and the enterprise of British shipowners'.

Despite the building of the *Oceanic* in 1899 by Harland and Wolff for the White Star Line to compete with the *Lucania* and *Campania*, the latter were able to maintain their lead until the building of the Norddeutscher Lloyd's *Kaiser Wilhelm Der Grosse* in 1897 and the *Kronprinz Wilhelm* in 1901.

With the building of these vessels, British lines lost their lead on the Atlantic run for the first time since the 1850s. Cunard could no longer find finances, as a private firm, to compete and in 1903, as a result of public pressure, the government lent £2,500,000 with an annual payment of £50,000 to pay for the *Lusitania* and the *Mauretania*, in return for a 25% interest in the company. The *Lusitania* was completed at Clydebank, now under the control of John Brown and Company, in 1907, and won the Blue Riband on her second voyage in that year. However, the *Mauretania* built by Swan-Hunter a little after her sister ship, proved a slightly faster vessel and retained the Blue Riband until 1929. On the other hand, the *Lusitania* seems to have been a better fitted ship, becoming very popular with American travellers. The Cunard Company, as a result of the success of these two vessels, ordered, with no financial aid from the Government, a larger but slower vessel, the *Aquitania*, completed by John Browns in 1914. The directors went to Clydebank because they had decided that comfort and size were more profitable than speed.

These record-breaking vessels for Atlantic services were largely built to meet the demands of passenger and fast mail traffic. After the early period little freight was carried and the ships restricted to the New York-Southampton run. There was, however, a demand for many other types of ship for use on the Atlantic and in other parts of the world, mostly to carry freight, a small number of first and second class passengers, and often large numbers of steerage emigrants. Even on the American routes to New York, Boston, and Philadelphia the larger firms like Cunard, the White Star, and the Hamburg-American lines had a share of this traffic. But it was for service over the longer routes to Canada, the West Indies, Suez, India, South Africa, and Australia that this demand was greatest. Here the requirement was for economy in fuel consumption and not for speed. The development of the compound engine in the 1860s and the triple expansion engine in the 1880s, principally by John Elder and Company, was to give Clyde yards a great share of these markets.

The Allan Line was formed in 1864, specifically to trade with the St Lawrence. The majority of the firm's vessels, up to 1914, were ordered from the Clyde yards of Alexander Stephen and Sons, D. & W. Henderson, and William Denny and Brothers, including the famous *Parisian* from Napiers, in 1881. This vessel, the earliest steel-hulled North Atlantic mail steamer, was designed to meet growing competition from other firms. The most celebrated company in the Canadian trade was certainly the Canadian Pacific Line, which had a special relationship with John Elder and Company, later Fairfields. In 1887, Sir William Pearce, the owner of the firm, founded the Canadian Pacific Steam Ship Line with G. E. Dodwell. The first vessels to be used by this line were the modernised ex-Cunarders, the *Abyssinia*, the *Batavia* and the *Parthia*, which Pearce had taken in part exchange for new ships. The line was only regarded as a temporary measure until the Canadian Pacific Railway could bring its own vessels into service in the Pacific. With the death of Pearce in 1891, the Canadian Pacific Steam Ship Line's interests merged with the Canadian Pacific Line. Although the first contract from this new company went to Barrow in 1891, thereafter most of the famous 'Empresses' were built at Fairfields, including the Empresses of Britain and Ireland in 1906, and the Empresses of Russia and Asia in 1913.

Long distance steamship services were pioneered by the P. and O. Line's development of routes to India and the Far East. At first P. and O. established two separate routes, one from Britain to Alexandria, and the other from Suez to India. From 1867 to 1915, the Clyde yards of Cairds, Stephens, Denny and Thomsons built no fewer than 76 ships for this firm, the majority coming from Cairds. With the opening of the Suez Canal in 1869 single journeys to both India and Australia became possible and other companies were able to break into the market. P. and O. lost ground, largely because the company's conservatism had resulted in a failure to adopt twin screw steamers or compound engines. Their main competitors were the British India Steam Navigation Company on the Indian route, and the Orient Line on the Australian. The British India Steam Navigation Company was a west-of-Scotland firm with much of its tonnage built by Connells, Barclay-Curle, and Stephens. The Orient Line operated services to Australia via the Cape of Good Hope and back through the Suez Canal. The Line's first vessel, the *Austral*, was built by Elder in 1882, and in 1891, Napiers built the *Orphir*, the first twin-screw steamer to sail to Australia. The *Orphir* was a well equipped ship comparable to the best the Atlantic could offer, but unfortunately very expensive to run. As a result of the establishment of the Orient Line, P. and O., in 1881, ordered the *Rome* and the *Carthage* from Cairds and, in the face of growing competition, in 1887, the four successful Jubilees, the *Victoria* and *Britannia* from Cairds, and the other two from Belfast. Again, in 1892, Cairds built the *Himalaya* and the *Australia* for P. and O. to compete against the *Orphir*. The Orient Line did not again present a real challenge until 1902, when John Browns built the very successful *Orontes*. There were other competitors for freight traffic on the India route, especially the Glasgow owned City Line. The masters of all this firm's vessels were required to sign a pledge and join the Scottish Temperance League, and no liquor was allowed on board. Many of the City ships were built by Connells and Barclay Curle. India and Australia were not the only destinations in the East by way of the Canal. Burma offered rich pickings in timber, oil, and rice, which were largely exploited by the Henderson and Bibby Lines. All Henderson's ships were built either by the family firm of D. & W. Henderson or by William Denny of Dumbarton.

Of lesser importance, but of equal significance for Clyde shipbuilders, was the growth of the South African, Pacific, and West-Indian trade. The development of South African trade is largely inter-related with that of the Indian and Australian. With sail-assisted steamers it was more economical to make use of the Roaring Forties by going out to Australia, via the Cape of Good Hope, and returning by Suez. The competition between the Union and Castle Lines to South Africa followed the same pattern as the Atlantic story. The Union Line began in 1853, to be joined in fierce competition by Sir Donald Currie's Castle Line in 1877. The *Dunrobin Castle*, the first Clyde-built 'Castle' ship, by Napiers in 1876, beat the record of Currie's first ship the *Windsor Castle*. The Union Line replied with the Denny-built *German* in 1877, and in the same year Currie again went to Napiers for four more ships. In 1878 and 1879, the Union Line ordered two faster vessels, the *Pretoria* from Denny and the *Arab* from Thomsons. The competition continued, largely reflecting the developing expertise of Clyde shipbuilders. In 1890 Fairfields built the *Dunnottar Castle*, the fastest and much the best equipped South African vessel of her time. The Union Line again replied to the challenge with the beautiful Denny-built *Scot*, $1\frac{1}{2}$ knots faster than the *Dunnottar Castle*. Competition now slackened, Currie continued to build at Fairfields, with the *Tantallon Castle* in 1894, the *Dunvegan Castle* in 1896 and the *Carisbrook Castle* in 1898, though the Union Line changed to Harland and Wolff. In 1900 the Lines amalgamated to form the Union-Castle Line.

As with P. and O. on the Indian and Australian routes, the Pacific was dominated by one company. The Pacific Steam Navigation Company was started by William Wheelwright, a merchant in Valparaiso. From the outset the firm had close connections with the Clyde. In 1846 the firm bought the iron paddler *Ecuador* from Tod and MacGregor to allow the development of the route between Callao and Panama. This gave the firm direct contact, overland, with the Royal Mail Steam Packet Company's West Indian Service. The most serious problem for the company was the shortage and expense of coal in the Pacific. By the 1850s the firm's financial situation was grave and the need for more economic vessels acute. The development of the compound engine by John Elder and Company saved the firm which ordered in 1856 from Elder the *Valparaiso*, the first really successful vessel fitted with compound engines. Such was the efficiency of this vessel that shortly afterwards all the firm's older ships were re-engined by Elder.

Several more orders for Elders followed, all four ships ordered in 1869 and three out of the five vessels between 1870 and 1872. In 1874 Elder built the *Iberia* and *Liguria*, at the time the finest vessels in the world, except for the new Inman and White Star Atlantic liners. In the 1890s, however, the firm went to Belfast for new tonnage except for the *Oriana*, built by Barclay-Curle in 1906 and the *Orcoma* by Beardmore in 1908. The *Orcoma*, known as 'the electric ship' being fitted with the latest electrical gadgetry, was the fastest and biggest ship in the Pacific. Although not in competition with the Pacific Steam Navigation Company, the New Zealand Shipping Company, late in the 19th century, opened up the steamer services in the south of the ocean terminating at New Zealand. Again, the main tonnage came from the Clyde yards. Elder built the firm's first five vessels in 1883-84. Thereafter Elder shared the orders with Denny, except for one vessel from Hawthorn-Leslie of Newcastle in 1902. However, the Shaw-Savill Line, the New Zealand Shipping Company's main competitor, ordered only two of their steam vessels from the Clyde, the *Arowa* and *Tainui* from Denny in 1884-85. Thereafter the line went to Belfast and Swan-Hunter.

The West Indies and South American trade was similarly dominated by one line, the Royal Mail Steam Packet Company, founded by James MacQueen in 1839. From the outset the firm came to Glasgow for its tonnage. Of the first 13 vessels ordered between 1841 and 1843, six were built in Clyde yards. The next five vessels came from elsewhere, but thereafter the firm had a continuous relationship with the Clyde until 1906, when the firm, like many others, went to Belfast. In 1852 the firm bought from Steeles, while building, the *La Plata*, the sister ship of Cunard's *Arabia*. From 1854 until 1906, 16 out of 20 of the firm's new ships were bought from the Clyde yards of Cairds, Elder and Napier, except for one vessel from Inglis, and one from Thomson. The Royal Mail Line was not without competitors: the Nelson Line, founded in 1910, quickly managed effectively to challenge the company on the River Plate run. Six out of ten of this firm's first vessels were built by Russells at Port Glasgow. The development of the banana trade with the West Indies, and the meat trade with the Argentine, firstly by the Imperial Direct West India Line, and then by Elder and Fyffes, led to the development of a Clyde specialization in refrigerated ships, largely by Stephens and Russells. Elder and Fyffes ordered one of their first ships, the *Comito*, from Stephens in 1915.

Although, after the 1860s, the Clyde is best known for its famous ocean liners, Clyde shipyards continued to compete in the market for estuarial, cross-channel, and other steamers designed for short voyages. Competition in this market was severe as many small yards could build these vessels to a high standard. Following the success of the *Margery* and *Rob Roy* numerous orders came to the Clyde; but with the development of steam shipbuilding in other areas, especially on the Thames, Mersey, and Tyne, companies tended to purchase vessels from their own localities. The North Lancashire Steam Navigation Company ordered the first three vessels for its Fleetwood service to the north of Ireland from Tod and MacGregor and Cairds, between 1844 and 1870; thereafter, until 1878, it ordered elsewhere. This pattern is typical of many other companies; but with the growing reputation of the Clyde for marine engineering and steel shipbuilding in the 1880s, yards in other areas found it increasingly difficult to compete for prestige passenger vessels. The Clyde's reputation for building vessels of this type rested largely on the development work of John Elder and Sir William Pearce. Some companies, such as the Isle of Man Steam Packet Company and Zeeland Steam Ship Company, had always had the majority of their vessels built on the Clyde; of 16 vessels built for the Zeeland Steam Ship Company between 1865 and 1909 all but two were built on the Clyde. In 1886 and 1887 the *Queen Victoria*, and *Prince of Wales* were built for the Isle of Man, Liverpool and Manchester Steam Ship Company by Fairfields, to compete with the new tonnage of the Isle of Man Steam Packet Company. These vessels made it possible for the first time to sail from Liverpool to the Isle of Man and back in one day and also have several hours ashore. In 1890 Fairfields built the *Adder* for G. and J. Burns' first daylight service between Greenock and Belfast.

In the 1890s twin-screw cross-channel ferries begain to replace paddle steamers. J. and G. Thomson were the pioneers, building, in 1891, three twin-screw steamers for the Channel Islands service of the London and South Western Railway Company, and in 1894, the twin-screw steamers *Columbia* and *Alva* for the same company's night service between Southampton and Le Havre. The *Columbia* and *Alva* were the first cross-channel vessels to have cabin berths; previously passengers slept in the dining saloon. During the same period, Thomsons built the *Glen Sannox*, one of the most famous paddle steamers ever, for the Glasgow and South Western Railway. She was the fastest Clyde steamer of her day with a speed of 19 knots.

The next major breakthrough came with the building by Dennys of the *King Edward* in 1901, the first commercial turbine steamer, built for a syndicate composed of the Parsons Marine Steam Turbine Company Ltd, Dennys, and Captain John Williamson, an established Clyde steamer operator. George Blake describes the introduction of this vessel in his book *The Westering Sun*, 'When the day came for her to slip down the ship-channel into deep water, the shores along some forty miles of coast were dotted with groups of elderly persons focusing her shape through telescopes and antique field-glasses; some were admiring her speed through the water, others prophesying (and rather hoping) that she would blow up'. The building of the *King Edward*, an event for steamer operators as significant as that of the *Dreadnought* for foreign navies, was followed by many further orders for similar vessels from Dennys. The *Queen*, built for the South Eastern and Chatham and the *Brighton*, built for the London, Brighton and South Coast Railways, by Dennys in 1903, were the first turbine cross-channel steamers in the world. Dennys built a further seven similar vessels between then and 1911. The success of these ships finally spelt the doom of cross-channel paddle steamers.

The Clyde's importance as a centre for the building of fast packet ships in the 1860s attracted the attention of the Confederacy during the American Civil War. Between 1861 and 1862 no fewer than 27 Clyde-built vessels were converted and sold to the South as blockade runners. Most of the shipyards on the river shared in the orders for ships especially designed to run the blockades, Simons building the *Rothesay Castle*, Elders the *Falcon*, *Flamingo*, *Ptarmigan*, *Condor* and the *Evelyn*. The contract for the building of the *Pampero* between the Confederacy and Thomsons attracted the attention of the Emancipation Society of Glasgow. The society protested to Earl Russell and the ship was seized on her way down the Clyde to her trials at Bowling Harbour on the instructions of the Lord Advocate. Stephens had built the *Shenandoah*, as the *Sea King*, the first composite screw steamer, designed to compete with the tea clippers on the voyage from China to Britain. This vessel was renamed *Shenandoah* when she was fitted as a commerce raider for the Confederacy, destroying, during her career, 37 Northern vessels.

Despite the importance of the development of steamship building on the Clyde, many famous sailing ships were built on the river until the early 20th century. Indeed the newer yards of Elders, Browns, and Dennys which had largely been formed to build steam ships, did construct iron sailing vessels during times of depression. The principal builders were Russells, Stephens, Charles Connell, Archibald MacMillan and Sons, and Scotts. Up to the mid 1850s the clipper trade to Australia and China was largely dominated by American firms operating American built ships. In 1856, however, the *Lord of the Isles*, built by Scotts to reply to this challenge, 'beat two of the fastest American clippers of almost twice her tonnage'. In 1856 the *Serica*, *Taeping*, and *Ariel*, built by Steeles of Greenock, the *Taitsing*, built by Connells, and the Liverpool-built *Fiery Cross*, took part in the most famous China tea-clipper race. The race was almost neck and neck all the way from Foo Chow and finished with the *Taeping*, *Ariel* and *Serica*, all docking in London on the same tide. The celebrated *Cutty Sark* was built at the little known Dumbarton yard of Scott and Linton, in 1869. This vessel was not as fast as many of her competitors, and probably owes her enormous reputation to her preservation at Greenwich. The Stephens-built *Maulsden* of the Dundee Clipper Line, in the 1870s 'staggered the nautical world by running from Greenock to Marybrough (Queensland) in 70 days'.

In 1897 the four-masted barque *Benares*, built by Murrays of Port Glasgow in 1897, made a record breaking voyage of 48 days between Cape Town and New York. Perhaps the finest testimony to Clyde-built sailing is in the novel *The Shadow Line* by Joseph Conrad, when describing going on board to *Otago*, a Stephens-built boat: 'her hull, her rigging, filled my eye with great content . . . at the first glance I saw that she was a high class vessel, a harmonious creature in the lines of her fine body, in the proportioned tallness of her spars. Whatever her age and her history she had preserved the stamp of her origin'.

Clyde-built sailing vessels gained a high reputation for speed and elegance, but many owners came to the river for less glamorous ships, such as bulk carriers for the Australian grain, Chilean nitrate, oil and other trades. Vessels built by such firms as Russell & Co were noted for their economy in operation, which led to their remaining competitive with steamships on long routes until the general introduction of the triple expansion engine in the 1890s. From the mid-1880s, Russell & Co, later Lithgows Ltd, had the largest annual output of any Clyde yard.

Although the proportion of naval ships constructed on the Clyde up to the 1880s was small, many of the naval vessels built on the river were significant. Scotts of Greenock built their first naval ship, *The Prince of Wales*, a sloop of war, in 1803. The vulnerability of paddle steamers and their unsuitability for long cruises made the Admiralty reluctant to adopt steam propulsion for ships of war, although paddle steamers were used from the 1830s for towing line-of-battle ships. In 1839 Scotts engined the *Hecate* and *Hecla*, the first naval vessels to be engined in Scotland. Between 1843 and 1876 Robert Napier and Sons built 30 hulls and 58 sets of engines for the Admiralty, and six hulls and 27 sets of engines for other governments. By 1878 one twelfth of Admiralty steam vessels had been built on the Clyde. The Admiralty was often criticised by contemporary commentators for failing to adopt innovations. Writing in 1861 Edward O. Hallstead in a series of lectures to the Royal United Service Institute strongly condemned the Admiralty for failing to build more iron ships of war. The Admiralty, though, had conducted several experiments on the effects of shot on iron hulls and the results were hardly encouraging. As far as the Clyde was concerned the Admiralty was quick to try out new techniques developed on the river. In 1848-49 Scotts engined their first iron ocean frigate, the *Greenock*, the largest warship of the day. In the same year Robert Napier built the *Simoon*, originally engined by Boulton and Watt. The Admiralty conducted a series of gun trials in 1850 on targets, representing sections of the hull of the *Simoon*, which were interpreted as confirming the reticence to adopt iron universally. In 1856 Napier built the *Erebus* and *Terror*, the first armoured monitors, which were intended to take part in the Baltic campaign of the Crimean War. In 1862 Napier launched the *Black Prince*, the second iron-clad British battleship. In the following year John Elder built the first naval compound engine for the *Constance*, whose comparative trial with the *Arethusa* and the *Octavia* – being both vessels of about the same tonnage as the *Constance*, (between 3,000 and 3,200 tons) but equipped with simple engines – fully demonstrated the superiority of the compound engine. Indeed, the yard of John Elder and Company became recognised as one of the leading naval yards in Britain. Chief Engineer King of the United States Navy wrote in 1877: 'of the thirty-seven engineering works and large shipbuilding works on the Clyde, the Fairfield works is now the most extensive and important . . . This firm is justly regarded as the pioneer of the compound system and the productions

18

are accepted as the best type'. In 1878 John Elder and Company built the *Nelson* and Robert Napier and Sons the sister ship, the *Northampton*, ocean-cruising broadside armour-plated ships, 'fitted with twin-screws each to be driven by an independent pair of compound engines'. In the same year John Elders built 'the most powerful marine engines ever constructed, for the extraordinary sum of £120,000', for the battleship *Inflexible*.

From the 1880s Naval orders tended to come in batches, usually in response to public pressure for the strengthening of the Navy to meet the French threat at home, and to police trade routes in an expanding Empire. In 1884 W. T. Stead, editor of the **Pall Mall Gazette**, campaigned for 'up-to-date battleships for the first line, fast cruisers for commerce protection and torpedo boats'. The Government succumbed to this pressure and ordered two first-class iron clads, five armoured cruisers, six torpedo cruisers and 14 torpedo boats. Seven of the torpedo cruisers were built by J. and G. Thomson; the first, HMS *Scout*, was a prototype for the *Archer* class of cruiser, fitted with ten torpedo tubes. These vessels, the predecessors of the torpedo boat destroyer, were largely unsuccessful and quickly withdrawn from service. In 1885 J. and G. Thomson built their first torpedo boat destroyers, the *Wiborg*, for the Russian Navy, and the *El Destructor*, for the Spanish Navy. The *Wiborg* could fire three torpedos simultaneously and had two Hotchkiss guns to destroy an attacking vessel of the same type. So that she could retreat rapidly after an attack her speed astern was 16 knots, three-quarters of her forward speed. In the same year J. and G. Thomson built a first class cruiser, the *Reina Regente*, for the Spanish Navy, one of the first cruisers with a protective deck.

By 1888 British Naval strength had fallen well behind France and Russia. Had war broken out with France, the Channel and Foreign Stations would have had to be seriously weakened to give equality in the Mediterranean. Admiral Bacon in his *Naval Scrapbook* wrote, 'There is no doubt that had we gone to war with France in those days we might well have been swept off the face of the globe. The Naval Defence Act saved the country'. This Act, which resulted from public realisation of our relative weakness again brought orders to the Clyde. Two scouting cruisers of the *Magicienne* type were ordered from John Elder and Company, and from J. and G. Thomson, two cruisers for protecting Australia, the *Tauranga* and *Ringarooma*, and also three second class cruisers, the *Terpsichore*, *Thetis* and *Tribune*.

The Naval Defence Act of 1889 marked the beginning of the modern race in Naval armaments. As a result from 1891-96 19 first-class battleships were ordered, two, the *Ramillies* and *Jupiter*, from J. and G. Thomson, and the engines for another, the *Barfleur*, from Scotts. By 1893, despite the provisions of the Naval Defence Act, Britain was again in trouble, largely as a result of the Franco-Russian alliance and the technical superiority of their vessels. The Gladstone government was unwilling to become committed to a large building programme. However, Gladstone resigned in March largely on this issue and Rosebery took his place. The minimum programme to give parity with the French was immediately approved. Many of the new vessels were ordered from Clyde yards, three torpedo boat destroyers and two cruisers from Fairfields, and three torpedo boat destroyers and one cruiser HMS *Terrible* from Thomsons. HMS *Terrible* was designed by Lord Fisher and William White, Director of Naval Construction, and was the progenitor of Fisher's battlecruisers. A lull in naval construction followed, but the international crisis of 1896 resulted in a revised building programme. A new class of battleship was introduced, designed to pass through the Suez Canal. The first ship of this class, the *Canopus*, was built at Portsmouth; but engined by Scotts of Greenock. One cruiser, a set of engines, and three torpedo boat destroyers were ordered from Thomsons. The object was still to achieve parity with the French and Russians and each new international crisis brought fresh orders to the Clyde. Between 1895 and 1901 Fairfields built 19 naval vessels of all descriptions out of a total production of 40 ships. In 1902 two battleships were ordered from the Clyde, the *Commonwealth*, from Fairfields, and the *Hindustan*, from John Browns at Clydebank. In addition John Browns made the engines for the *Africa*, built in the same programme at Chatham. This massive building programme in the years prior to 1902 gave Britain an undeniable superiority and the years between 1902 and 1906 saw a dramatic fall in orders. Fairfields only built four naval vessels out of a total production of 25 ships.

However, in 1904, Lord Fisher's appointment as First Lord of the Admiralty was marked by sweeping reforms: the scrapping of many obsolete ships and the reconstruction of the naval administration, largely in response to demands for a decrease in naval expenditure. As Arthur Marder writes, 'Fisher wanted to scrap all warships in commission or in reserve which were deemed too weak to fight or too slow to run away'. The victory of Japan in 1904, in the Russo-Japanese war, saw the eclipse of Russia as a great naval power. The danger was now from the new German navy. Fisher was determined to meet this threat at once and for all by building a new class of battleship, the Dreadnoughts, the fastest and the most powerful battleships afloat and the first turbine-engined large naval vessels. Fisher also wished to complement these battleships with new battlecruisers, a vessel, described by him as, 'greyhounds of the sea', my 'new testament ships', and 'hares to catch tortoises'. Two of the first batch of these ships were built on the Clyde, between 1906 and 1908, the *Inflexible*, at Clydebank, and the *Indomitable* at Fairfields. Fisher was not content to allow the design of his new ships to remain static but experimented with new designs, especially in hull forms and turret arrangements, in the years between 1906 and his retirement in 1910. The engines of the third generation Dreadnought, the *Bellerophon*, were built by Fairfields in 1907, and the engines of three of the 1909 Dreadnoughts were made on the Clyde. The first Dreadnoughts to be built on the Clyde were the *Colossus*, at Scotts, and the *Conqueror*, at Beardmores, in 1909. Between 1911 and 1914 five Dreadnoughts were ordered from Clyde yards (including the *Barham*), two battlecruisers, and two sets of battlecruisers' engines from John Browns.

Fisher was not only concerned to improve the design of large capital ships but also the smaller, equally essential, fleet escorts – the destroyers, light cruisers, and torpedo boats. Between 1903 and 1912, 14 light cruisers, 49 destroyers and 30 torpedo boats

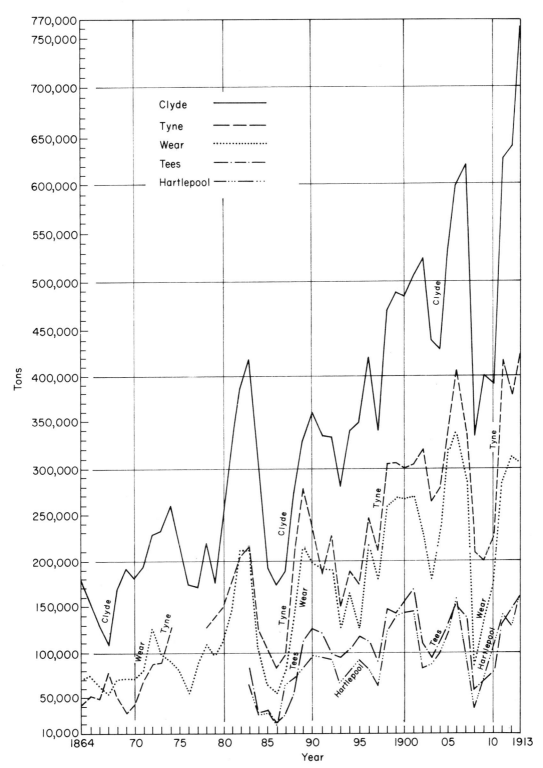

Diagram showing total production on the Clyde, Tyne, Wear, Tees, and at Hartlepool.

21

were ordered from a variety of Clyde yards. In 1905 Yarrow and Company, specialists in torpedo boat and destroyer work, decided to move to Scotstoun, an event of great significance for Clyde shipbuilders. From his time in the Admiralty in 1892 Fisher had acquired a high regard for Sir Alfred Yarrow's ability to design such ships. It was probably the presence of Yarrows on the Clyde that made for such a high output of these vessels from other yards on the river, such as Inglis, Dennys and the London and Glasgow Shipbuilding and Engineering Company. The first submarine to be built in Scotland was the S1 by Scotts between 1912 and 1914. Thereafter during the First World War submarines were built by several yards including Dennys, Browns and Fairfields. A variety of other Admiralty craft was also built by the smaller yards just before and during the First World War, including Insect class gunboats by Barclay Curle and Lobnitz, and paddle troopships for the Mesopotamian campaign. The output of all the Clyde yards during the First World War was greater than any other shipbuilding area in Britain. Between 1914 and 1919 Fairfields alone built 54 Admiralty ships, 32 torpedo boats, one battleship, one battlecruiser, ten submarines, four minesweepers and three cruisers.

The expansion of shipbuilding and marine engineering on the Clyde in the 19th century was reflected in the rapid growth of Glasgow and the rise of a wealthy business community who could afford expensive hobbies. Many bought remote estates in the West Highlands which were most easily reached by steam yachts. One of the first men to order such a yacht was Thomas Assheton Smith, a member of the Royal Yacht Squadron, who bought the *Menai* from David Napier in 1830. This purchase led to his expulsion from the Squadron, as the other members disapproved of 'steam'. Undeterred, he continued to order successive yachts from Napiers, most outstanding the *Fire King* of 1839 reputed to have been the fastest vessel afloat. As with steam packets, all yards shared in this market. Among the most famous yachts built on the river were those built at Fairfields in the 1880s, including a circular yacht, the *Livadia* for the Tzar of Russia in 1881, designed by Admiral Popoff to give complete protection from submarine explosions. The series of *Lady Torfridas*, built by the firm for its managing directors Sir William Pearce and later his son Sir William G. Pearce, were the largest of their time. When Sir William Pearce became a member of Parliament, he sailed to the House of Commons to take his seat, anchoring his yacht outside the Houses of Parliament to demonstrate the quality of Clyde workmanship. Thomsons built several equally famous yachts including the *Mayflower*, in 1896, later to become the Presidential yacht of the United States of America.

Although there were several firms of boatbuilders on the Clyde specializing in sailing yachts, some of the shipbuilders also constructed large craft of this type. D. & W. Henderson of Meadowside, normally merchant ship builders, in the late 19th century built a succession of very famous yachts including the America's Cup challengers *Thistle* (1887) *Valkyrie* II (1893) and *Valkyrie* III (1895). The *Thistle* was purchased by the German Emperor Wilhelm II, and renamed *Meteor*. The Prince of Wales (later Edward VII) also owned a Henderson-built yacht, the *Britannia* (1893).

It would be misleading to suggest that the 19th century was a period of sustained growth for the Clyde shipbuilding industry. As the graph of the annual tonnage produced illustrates, the industry was subject to the classical symptoms of booms and violent depressions, characteristically accompanied by industrial disputes. During the century the industry developed standard reactions to the onset of either a boom or depression. In a depression material prices fell, wage rates were cut, often with the agreement of the work force, and unprofitable contracts were accepted. In November 1874 the Clyde Shipbuilders Association resolved that, 'the present position of trade justified the reduction of the rate of wages of fifteen per cent'. In 1885, a year described in the magazine *Engineering*, as one that 'will long be looked back on as one of very great depression in the Clyde shipbuilding industry', John Elder contracted to build the *Campania* at a very low tender which resulted in the disastrous loss of £40,514. Such losses were uncharacteristic, but because competition for contracts, except at the height of a boom, was always severe, profit margins were never large, usually between 10 and 15 per cent. Industrial disputes, although adding to a company's problems only appear to have severely distorted the position in the years 1866 and 1877. The strike of ship-carpenters, iron-workers, platers, riveters and boiler-makers, in 1877, resulted in a lock-out which lasted for eight months, putting 10,000 men out of work. Industrial action, however, never seems to have resulted in a serious loss of confidence in Clyde yards. In 1867 a writer in *Engineering* confidently predicted that, 'with revival of trade generally, and especially the termination of strikes for a time at least, the Clyde builders are certain to receive large orders'.

The marked effect of the trade cycle on the industry's output is a reflection of the direct relation of shipbuilding to world trade, for, with the onset of a depression in trade, orders for ships fell off and occasionally contracts were cancelled. Moreover, the severity of the onset of a depression was often aggravated by rising raw material prices, wages, and costly reinvestment programmes, undertaken by the yards to meet projected future demand, resulting in sharp increases in on-costs and contract prices. All these were problems of which the Clyde shipbuilders were aware, but which were recognized as being insoluble. As the outline of the relationship between Clyde shipbuilding and the development of steamer services demonstrates, the success of the Clyde in dominating world markets resulted largely from the continuing process of innovation, ranging from the important developments of the triple expansion engine to simple innovations like the introduction of wire rigging. However, continuous innovation demands rapid re-capitalization which, in return, requires long-term finance and a full order book to provide cash to meet interest payments. Unfortunately it was normally at the time when the shipyard needed most orders to fulfil these commitments that the boom collapsed. It was for this reason that yards specializing in steam vessels, like J. and G. Thomson and John Elder were prepared to build square-rigged sailing ships during the 1875 to 1879 depression. During depressions freight rates fell and shipowners were therefore anxious to build the most economical vessels. In 1860, with the development of the more economic compound engine, the depressions were not characterized by any marked decrease in orders for steam vessels from the Clyde. Owners were anxious to rid themselves of uneconomic, simple-engined vessels in preference for compound engined vessels which gave better profit margins on freight. In the 1875–1879 depression the position was different: steamers had penetrated the long routes to China and Australia but had not proved significantly more economical than sailing vessels. With the onset of the depression many owners reverted to sail and, significantly, throughout this period, and into the 1890s, Russells of Port Glasgow, a yard specializing in sailing vessels, launched the greatest·tonnage of any Clyde yard. All this had serious repercussions for builders like Thomsons and Elder who had invested in new plant, premises and equipment to build large ships propelled by triple expansion engines. In the long term this investment was justified; but in the short the effect was disastrous. Despite the recovery of 1888-89, Thomsons had, by November 1889, run into grave financial difficulties. The partners wrote to their accountant, William MacKinnon, on 22 November, 'From various causes the results have fallen short of what might have been reasonably expected; but we think we may confidently state that we are now entering a time when, through fuller employment and from experience acquired in recent years in the building of vessels of great size and speed, we shall be able to overcome the difficulties which caused disappointment in the past and to show results more commensurate with the value and capability of the works'. Despite these sentiments, to avoid bankruptcy the firm became a limited company in 1890 to raise a debenture mortgage to pay off the bank overdraft.

The only solution to these problems was, during depressions, to seek Admiralty contracts, or Government subsidized contracts, which were not subject to normal market pressures. It is interesting to note that a large proportion of Admiralty contracts came to Clyde yards in bad years, and HMS *Nelson* and *Northampton* to Elder and Napier respectively, in 1878, and HMS *Terrible* to Clydebank, in 1893. Moreover, it was during depressions that the Admiralty was under pressure to build more vessels as trade depression tended to result in increased protection of established markets and the penetration of new ones. However, Admiralty contracts, in this period, did not provide easy profits; competition for them was fierce and many yards lost heavily as a result. But this was preferable to the dispersal of a yard's skilled labour force and, in any event, the losses were never larger than those which would have resulted from the failure to pay interest on bank loans. In many ways the shipbuilders' problems were not unlike those of today. In 1873 J. and G. Thomson wrote to Cunard asking for extra payments for the *Bothnia* and *Scythia*, as the constructional programme was behind resulting from 'the contractors for the new yard being greatly behind the specified time for having the buildings complete'.

3 The first iron trans-Atlantic mail steamer, PS *Persia* is
shown here on the ways at Robert Napier's shipyard at Govan
in 1855. Although she had a high fuel consumption she carried
250 passengers, and had a speed of 13 knots, which allowed
her owners, Cunard, to compete effectively with the Collins
line. Her clipper bow saved her from sinking when she hit an
iceberg on her maiden voyage.

4   The PS *Industry* at the end of her days. This famous early Clyde paddle steamer was built in 1814 by Fife of Fairlie, and her hulk was still visible in Bowling Harbour in 1924. Her engine (the second) survives, dismantled, in store in Glasgow.

5   Probably the earliest surviving photograph of an Atlantic liner, this view of the PS *Arabia* shows her fitting out at Robert Napier's Lancefield Dock in 1853. Built for the British and North American Royal Mail Steam Packet Company (Cunard) by Steeles of Greenock, she was the last wooden paddle steamer built for Cunard and the first with tubular boilers. Her service speed was $12\frac{1}{2}$ knots and she carried 180 passengers, but unfortunately she was very expensive to run, burning nearly twice as much coal as her predecessor, the PS *Asia*. In the foreground are piles of pig-iron awaiting shipment.

6 *above left* TSS *City of New York*, seen here in the fitting-out basin at Clydebank, and her sister ship, the *City of Paris*, were the first twin screw passenger liners on the North Atlantic. Although sails were retained the twin screws permitted them to cross the Atlantic unassisted. These very successful ships, with a speed of 19½ knots, were built for the Inman International Line, by then under American control. No expense was spared to make these vessels the finest afloat. The large dome forward of the bridge is the roof of the dining room.

7 *left* Built by William Denny and Brothers for the Loch Lomond Steamship Company, in 1862, the PS *Prince Consort* is seen here at Ardlui Pier on Loch Lomond. The saloon is a later addition. Steamers such as these carried wealthy businessmen who had built houses on the 'Bonnie Banks', such as Sir James Lumsden, Lord Provost of Glasgow in the 1860s.

8 *above* This curious vessel is the Russian torpedo boat, Wiborg, built by J. & G. Thomson in 1886. She was designed with a high speed astern, so that after firing her Whitehead torpedo she could move quickly out of range of the enemy. The torpedo-boat destroyer was developed from this ship and her contemporary, the Spanish Navy's *El Destructor*, also built by J. & G. Thomson.

9 Sir William G. Pearce's yacht *Lady Torfrida*, designed to cruise under sail or in steam and built by Fairfield in 1890. The Pearce family had a succession of vessels of this name, all of which were quickly sold to distinguished customers.

10 *below* The fitting-out basin at Clydebank in 1890. The sheer-legs on the left were used to lift heavy machinery on to vessels. The green fields in the background are there to this day. The vessels in the picture are (left to right) an unidentified coaster; one of three vessels built for the London & South Western Railway's Channel Island service; cruisers HMAS *Tauranga* and *Ringarooma*, ordered as HMS *Phoenix* and *Psyche*; and the Japanese cruiser *Chiyoda*, the first Japanese vessel with large quickfiring guns.

11 A superb photograph of the SS *Friesland* on trials in the Firth of Clyde. The last important Atlantic liner with a clipper bow, she was built by J. & G. Thomson for the Red Star Line, a subsidiary of the American International Mercantile Marine Company, which also owned the White Star and Inman lines. Designed to carry 600 steerage as well as 328 first and second class passengers, she was a marked improvement on earlier Red Star vessels.

12 PS *Adder* on trials in the Firth of Clyde. This vessel was built for Messrs. G. & J. Burn's Greenock–Belfast service by Fairfield, in 1890. Up to that time the firm had operated overnight only to Belfast. The *Adder* inaugurated a very popular daylight service. She was typical of several high-speed cross-channel steamers built by Fairfield in the '80s and '90s.

13 The *Vildanden*, a ship built for Bruusgaard, Kjosterud & Co, Drammen, Norway, by Russell & Co, Port Glasgow in 1891, awaiting trials in the Firth of Clyde.

14 On her way down river, TSS *Campania* which, with her sister ship the *Lucania*, both built by Fairfields in 1892, set new standards on the North Atlantic run, placing the Cunard Company once more in the lead. This photograph was taken from the top of the sheer-legs at Clydebank.

15 The *Severn*, a three masted auxiliary barque built for W. B. Willson, Baltimore, by Russell & Co. Port Glasgow 1892.

16 One of the most famous of the late Victorian Clyde steamers, the PS *Glen Sannox*, built by J. & G. Thomson, in 1892, for the Glasgow and South Western Railway's Ardrossan-Brodick service. Speed was obtained at the expense of a very high coal consumption. Her fine hull form was developed from model studies on the Forth and Clyde canal. She was the fastest Clyde paddle steamer of her day, and probably the most beautiful.

17 *above* Seen here on trials, the *Tantallon Castle*, built for Sir Donald Currie's Castle Line by Fairfield, in 1894, to compete with the Union Line's *Scot*. Note the continuing use of sails on ships used on the long voyage to South Africa.

18 The *Clan Galbraith*, a four-masted barque built for Thomas Dunlop, Glasgow, by Russell & Co, Port Glasgow 1895.

19 The America's Cup challenger *Valkyrie* III built for the Earl of Dunraven in 1895 by D. & W. Henderson. This vessel is typical of the fine yachts built in this yard.

20 *below* HMS *Diana*, a second-class cruiser completed by Fairfield in 1896. The ram bow and the absence of obvious armour are notable. One of a class of colonial cruisers built largely to offset the effects of economic depression, she is seen here on trials.

21 The schooner yacht *Rainbow* built by D. & W. Henderson in 1898 for Mr C. C. Orr-Ewing, a member of a well-known firm of calico printers.

23 A remarkable view of the Renfrew yards of Lobnitz and Company Limited and William Simons & Company, c. 1900, showing bucket dredgers and hopper barges under construction. There was intense rivalry between these firms, both of whom gained high reputations for dredgers and other harbour servicing craft. Twelve vessels can be seen here.

22 One of six 'thirty knotters' built by Fairfield between 1897 and 1900, HMS *Falcon*. These torpedo-boat destroyers exploited to the full the capabilities of the reciprocating marine steam engine. *Falcon* was sunk in a collision in 1918.

26 *above* One of the first batch of Admiral Fisher's battle-cruisers, HMS *Indomitable*, built by Fairfield in 1908, and designed to have 'a damned big six or seven knot surplus'. She had a speed of 25½ knots, and eight 12 inch guns. Note the torpedo-net booms along the side of the ship.

24 *above left* A scene on board HMS *Good Hope*, an armoured cruiser, completed by Fairfield in 1901. This view was taken during commissioning at Portsmouth and shows one of her two 9.2 inch guns. The vessel was built as a flag ship, and carried Joseph Chamberlain to South Africa to negotiate with the Boers in 1902. She was ultimately sunk with all hands in the battle of the Falkland Islands, in 1914, as Admiral Craddock's flag ship.

25 *left* The *River Clyde*, built by Russell & Co. in 1905 for Ormond, Cook & Co. This vessel subsequently became well known for her part in the Gallipoli campaign in 1915, where she acted as a landing craft.

27 *overleaf* The crowded fitting-out basin in Clydebank c. 1905 with (left to right) RMS *Carmania*, built for Cunard's Liverpool supplementary service which was mainly for third-class passengers; HMS *Antrim*, a Devonshire class armoured cruiser; and HMS *Hindustan*, a King Edward VII class pre-Dreadnought battleship.

28 HMS *Colossus*, the first Dreadnought built on the Clyde, completed by Scotts Shipbuilding & Engineering Company Limited in 1912. At Jutland she helped the *Collingwood* to sink the German battle-cruiser *Lützow*.

29 The famous and ill-fated *Lusitania*, built by Brown's at Clydebank, and seen here on her trials in 1907. This vessel and her Tyne-built sister, the *Mauretania*, held the Blue Riband of the Atlantic for many years. Her sinking, in 1915, by the submarine U20 was a factor in bringing the United States into the First World War.

30 TSS *Abhona*, built for the British India Steam Navigation Company in 1910 by Alexander Stephen and Sons. Many ships were built on the Clyde for this Scottish firm, founded by a group of Kintyre men in 1881. Though they were much smaller than contemporary Atlantic vessels the first-class passenger accommodation was of an equally high standard.

31 The first of the many diesel-engined vessels to be built on the Clyde, MV *Jutlandia*, completed by Barclay, Curle and Company for the East Asiatic Company Limited at their Clydeholm yard in 1912. She was fitted with engines built by the firm at Stobcross to designs by Burmeister and Wain, and had no funnel; the exhaust was led up one of the masts. Barclay, Curle had great faith in motor ships, and believed that they would be popular with passengers owing to the absence of smoke, soot and dirt.

32 HMS *Gnat*, an Insect class China river gunboat, built by Lobnitz and Company Limited in 1915. These shallow-draught vessels, with their curious side-by-side twin funnels, survived to be used in the Mediterranean during the Second World War.

33 *left* HMS *Swordfish*, the first steam submarine in the British Navy, completed by Scotts Shipbuilding & Engineering Company at Greenock in 1916. The K class was derived from this vessel.

34 *below left* Perhaps the most unusual class of submarine ever built, the Ks, which gained notoriety on the Clyde owing to the disastrous sinking of K13, in the Gareloch, on acceptance trials. The problems associated with the use of steam power in submarines were not solved till the nuclear age. Photographs of Ks with steam up are rare, hence the inclusion of this view of K2, built at Portsmouth Dockyard, at Clydebank in 1918.

35 *below* Paddle steamer P60 built for troop transport during the Mesopotamian campaign by Lobnitz and Company Limited in 1916. Like the Insect class of gunboats this is a shallow-draught vessel.

36 *overleaf* First World War camouflage applied to TSS *Ormonde*, built at Clydebank between 1913 and 1917. She was designed as a passenger liner, but was completed as a troopship. Geared turbines were fitted, unusual in merchant vessels of this period.

37 The cutting machine at William Denny & Brothers' test tank in Dumbarton. The wax model is being shaped by tools guided by a pointer moved along a scale drawing of the hull lines. This machine was invented by William Froude and built by the celebrated woodworking machine tool makers, John McDowall & Sons of Johnstone in 1884.

CONTRACT AND DESIGN

The contract for building a ship could be secured in open competition by submitting the lowest tender, but frequently competition was less than perfect. Yards developed special relationships with shipping companies, sometimes offering particularly favourable terms for payment; occasionally only one yard could tackle a particular contract. In any event, sketch designs with estimated prices would be submitted to a potential customer, and more detailed estimates and designs might have to be prepared before the order was secured. The contract would normally specify progress payments, and bonus or penalty payments for performance greater or less than that specified.

Builders of wooden ships normally worked out their designs on wooden half-models of existing vessels with minor modification. This practice was transferred to iron ship-building by such firms as Alexander Stephen and Sons Ltd. The hull form as worked out could then be transferred directly to the mould loft, a large covered area where the 'lines' of the ship (horizontal and vertical cross-sections) could be drawn to full size. The constraints placed on the building of iron ships for steam propulsion, especially after the introduction of Lloyds' rules, led to the working out on paper of hull lines, rather than on a solid model, and of expansion plans showing the sizes and shapes of the plates.

An important aid to ship design is the test tank, where model hulls may be tested for resistance to propulsion and behaviour in waves. The first model experiments with steamships were probably those made by David Napier on the mill-pond at his Camlachie works, but his technique was certainly crude compared with that adopted by William Denny and Brothers. This firm built the first test tank in Scotland in 1883, where they used techniques devised by William Froude in 1872. For tank tests, wax models are cast to approximate form and then the design lines are cut on the wax by machine. The form of the model may be altered as a result of tests, and the modified lines then taken and transferred to the mould loft.

As a ship is a large structure of complex shape it is exceedingly difficult, and indeed undesirable, to insist on exact adherence to the original design drawings. It is necessary to prepare drawings of the vessel as completed. These are known as 'as-fitted' drawings.

Apart from drawings of hull form, drawings of the internal structure must be prepared, with detailed drawings of fittings such as pipes. For prestige vessels, designs of accommodation were frequently prepared by outside specialists in interior decoration – the *Lusitania* interiors were designed by Glasgow architect James Miller – and in many cases the 'as fitted' plans and sections from the major yards show details of the accommodation, down to such details as door handles and buttons on upholstery.

53

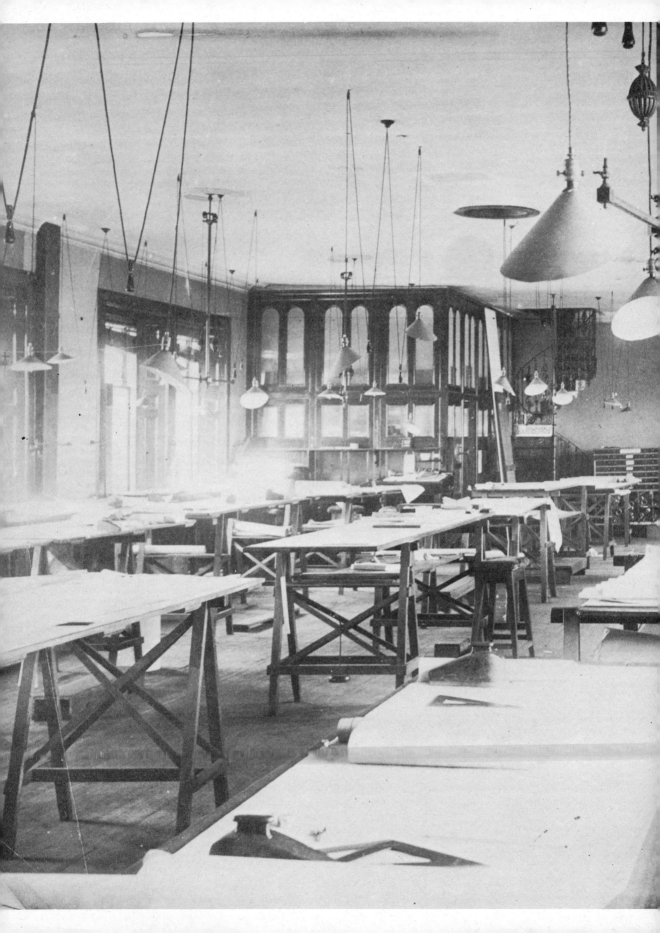

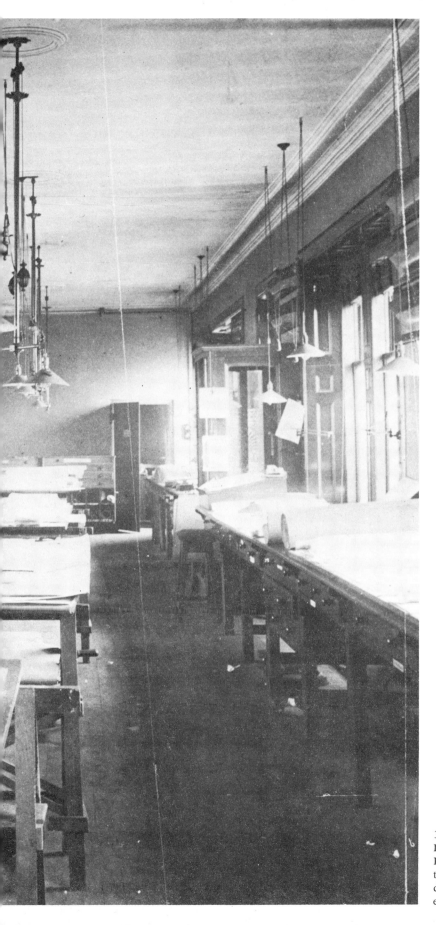

38 The ship drawing office at William Denny & Brothers' Leven Shipyard, Dumbarton, about 1900. The flat tables are characteristic of ship drawing offices to this day. Note the elaborately counter-balanced lamps.

39 Beardmore's shipyard drawing office at Dalmuir in 1911.

40 The test tank at Denny's. The curious appearance of the water is due to the lengthy exposure required by the slow photographic emulsions of the day. The steam engine on the right propelled the carriage on the left to which the model was attached.

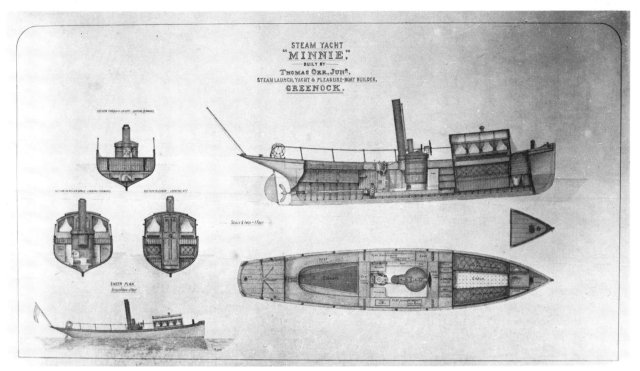

41 An 'as fitted' drawing of the small steam yacht *Minnie* built by the little-known firm of Thomas Orr, Junior of Greenock. The standard views are more clearly seen here than in drawings of larger vessels.

42 *above* The deck plating for a Brazilian destroyer laid out in the newly completed Boiler Shop at Yarrow's yard in 1907. This trial assembly has been made using bolts instead of rivets.

43 *overleaf* The mould loft at the Cartsburn Yard of Scotts Shipbuilding & Engineering Company Limited *c.* 1910. Here the templates for the frames and plates were prepared from full-sized drawings of the hull lines. Note the indirect electric arc lighting for night work.

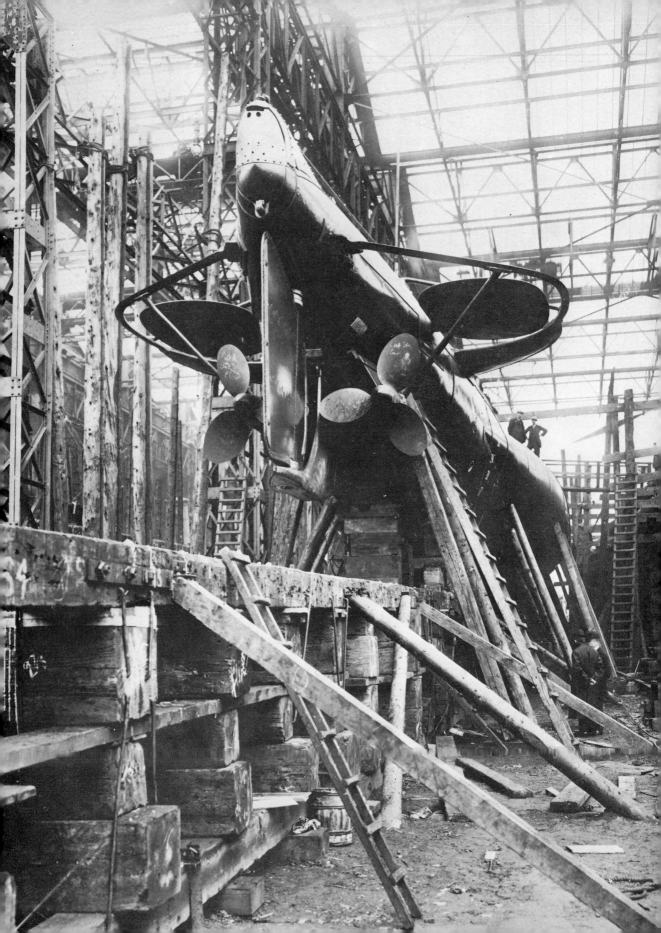

ON THE STOCKS

Construction of a riveted iron or steel ship began with the laying of the keel which could be of either the bar (projecting) type or the flat plate type, with an internal vertical keel. Next the floors, or vertical cross members of the ship's bottom, were added, and the bottom plated in order to provide extra strength. In the largest vessels the tops of the floors might be plated over to form a double bottom, a valuable safety measure. The upward extensions of the floors, the frames, were then added, and braced by longitudinal frames, known as stringers. At the ends of the keel, the stem and the stern frame were attached. The deck beams were then inserted, keeping the sides of the ship in place and acting as supports for the deck plates and loads. Vertical pillars were placed at intervals across the deck beams, linking the decks and giving them structural unity. The decks and sides could then be plated.

The parts of the ship mentioned had to be prepared in workshops before assembly on the building berth. The keel plates were cut to shape in a shearing machine, the rivet holes were punched, and the final forming might be done in a set of bending rolls. The shapes of the frames were transferred from the mould loft by constructing light wooden templates. Each of these was then laid out on the 'scrieve board', an iron plate with a gridiron of holes. Pegs were inserted in the holes nearest the template and washers added to give the exact profile. A length of iron or steel section with rivet-holes punched, was then heated and hammered up to the washers. At the same time the arm of the section to be riveted to the shell was bevelled out to the correct angle. Templates were also made in the mould loft for the plates, which were cut to shape by shears, rivet holes punched, then curved, if necessary, in shell bending rolls. Where a compound curved plate (that is plate curved in two directions) was required this was heated and hammered over a former. The forged stem, forged or cast steel stern post and the rudder frame were normally brought in from specialist firms. Assembly of the parts was by riveting, a process in which a short length of iron or steel rod, previously provided with a head, was heated to red heat and inserted through holes in overlapping pieces of metal. The protruding end of rod was then hammered over, forming a second head, making the rivet shank a tight fit in the holes, and bringing the pieces being joined into close contact. For much of the 19th century riveting was by hand, where a 'hauder on' held up a heavy hammer or a 'dolly' – a massive piece of iron – to the rivet head while 'riveters' hammered up. Rivets heated on a portable hearth were thrown to the riveter by a rivet boy. Hydraulic and pneumatic riveting machines were later introduced.

Apart from the construction of the shell, the propeller and some shafting were usually

61

44 Submarine E35 virtually complete at Clydebank c. 1916.
Note the hydroplanes for vertical steering of the boat under water. Preparation of the launching ways is well advanced.

fitted on the stocks, while in some cases fitting out went much further. Indeed there are cases on record of vessels being launched with steam up. In many instances, however, machinery could not be installed on the berth owing to lack of suitable cranes.

46 Bending a keel plate at Clydebank about 1900. This powerful hydraulic machine was designed by Hugh Smith and Company of Possil, Glasgow, to bend heavy plates for the largest type of ship. The open ends of the jaws permitted plates of any length to be worked.

45 *left* Wooden blocks in position prior to laying the keel of a ship at Fairfield *c.* 1900. The blocks were carefully aligned at the correct inclination for a smooth launch. In the background is the wooden walk-way provided to maintain the old-established public right-of-way along the river bank. It was removed prior to launching. Note the use of narrow-gauge railways for the handling of materials.

49 The keel-laying ceremony for HMS *Colossus* at Scotts Shipbuilding and Engineering Company, Greenock in 1909. The ceremonial closing of the first rivet is about to be performed. The first payment to the builder is made at this stage.

47 *above left* This view shows a bar keel in position at Clydebank, *c.* 1891, with the first floors in position. Note the curved keel end which will be fastened to the stem.

48 *left* The double bottom of RMS *Aquitania* at Clydebank in 1910. All the floors are in position, but plating of the tank top has not yet begun. In order to accommodate this enormous ship (901 feet long) two berths were knocked into one and extra piling had to be carried out. It was on this berth that the 'Queens' were built.

50 *above left* View of the east yard at Clydebank about 1910, with three vessels at different stages of construction. Framing of the ship on the right has just begun. Note that rigged derrick cranes are being introduced: the one on the right is incomplete.

51 *left* The framing shed at Denny's Leven Yard, Dumbarton. This was an up-to-date shed for its time, with adequate headroom and well-laid-out machinery. Note the frames in preparation in the foreground and the range of punching and shearing machines on the right.

52 Stern view of the *Kralj Aleksandar*, built by Lithgows in 1931 for Czechoslovakian owners. Although this is outside our period, the techniques are unchanged and the photograph illustrates clearly how the stern frames were built up on a riveted ship. Note the bossing for the propeller shafts, and the use of both wood and steel for scaffolding.

53 *left* Submarine E55 being erected at Denny's Leven Yard in 1916. The circular frames make an interesting contrast with those of a more conventional vessel. The E class was the principal type of submarine used by Britain during the First World War. This vessel narrowly missed the chance of intercepting Admiral Scheer's High Seas fleet after the battle of Jutland.

54 *below left* Drilling hull plates at Scotts' Cartsburn Yard, Greenock, about 1905. Pneumatic drills, by Consolidated Pneumatic Tools of Fraserburgh, are in use. The cylinders in the foreground are air receivers for the drills.

55 Shell plate rolls in use at Clydebank *c.* 1890. The rivet holes were punched or drilled before bending. On the left is an upstairs lavatory, freeing ground space for the manipulation of metal.

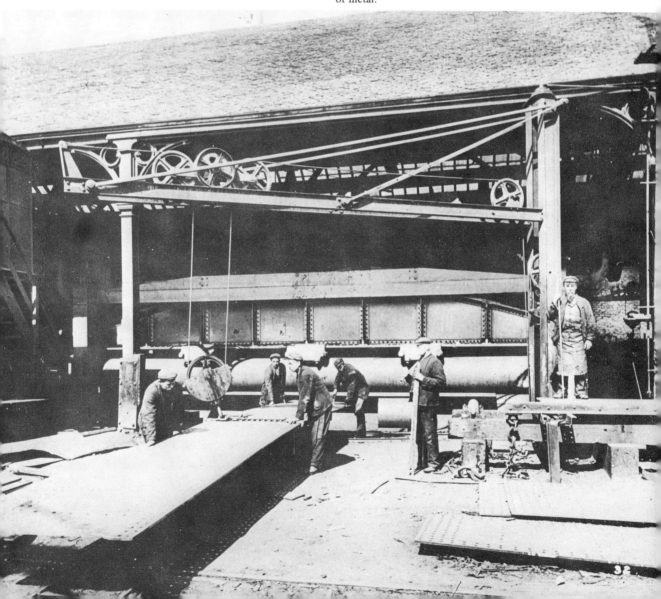

56 Hydraulic riveters at work on the hull of the *Lusitania* in 1906, riveting the uppermost strake of plating. Two types of riveting machine are in use, suspended from a counterbalanced beam mounted on a bogie.

57 The covered building berth at Fairfield, showing *Train Ferry No. 3* under construction in 1917. These ferries were built for transporting war materials to the Continent. Covered berths were used for smaller contracts in several yards. In this view the plating is well under way but much riveting remains to be done.

58 *right* The last stages of the hull construction of HMS *Argonaut*, a Diadem class protected cruiser at Fairfield in 1897. The wood sheathing was fitted over the main hull plating, in order to give protection against direct hits, and a layer of copper was applied to the wood to prevent decay and loss of speed due to marine growths.

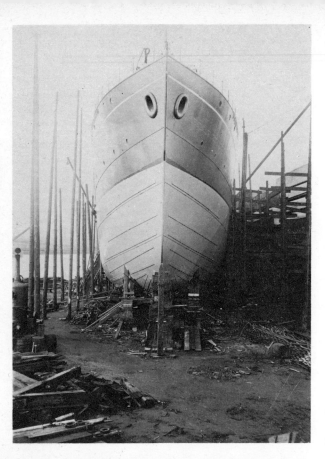

59 *left* An unidentified vessel on the ways at the Scotstoun yard of Charles Connell & Co in about 1900. Note the complete absence of cranes, and the drag chains to the left and right of the hull.

60 *right* Propellers were fitted before launching, and this view at Clydebank shows a large built-up propeller being bored to take the shaft. Built-up propellers were fairly rare, as they were normally cast in one piece.

61 *below* The monitor HMS *Sir John Moore* almost complete on the ways at Scotts' Cartsburn yard in 1915. The curious underwater shape was designed to give the vessel shallow draught and stability for inshore bombardment in support of invasion.

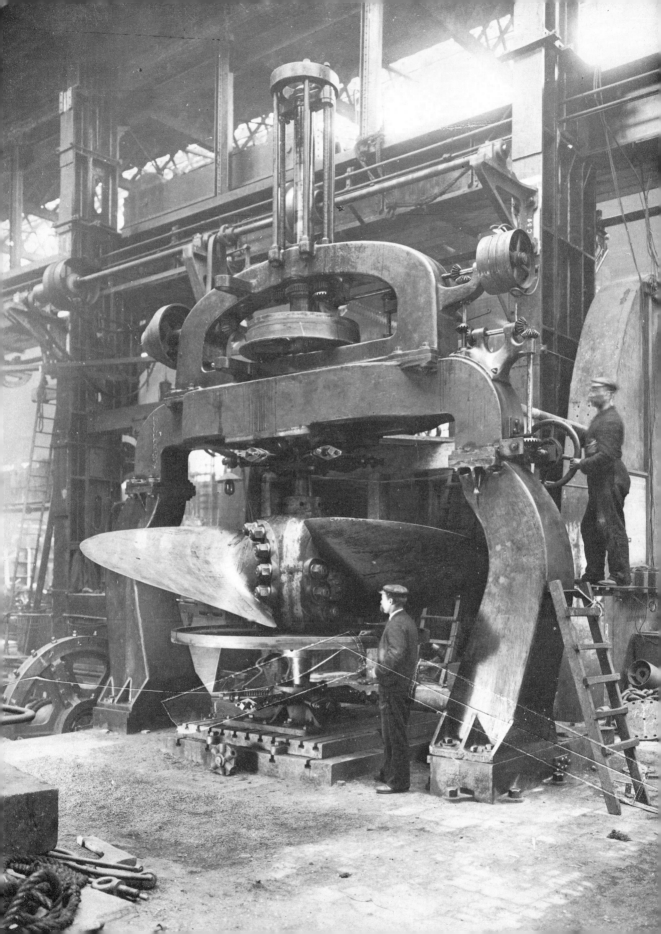

LAUNCHING

Ships are usually built on a prepared berth, with piles driven into the soil, supporting cross baulks of timber or reinforced concrete ways. During construction the ship rests on centrally placed keelblocks, assisted by shores and bilgeblocks (side supports). When the ship is ready to be launched, its weight must be transferred from these supports to 'sliding ways' which slide on greased 'standing ways' supported by the piles. The standing ways are inclined to allow the vessel to slide. Additional support is given at the bow and stern by the fore and after 'poppets' – wooden cradles held to the ship by ropes. The fore poppets take the load thrown on the bow of the ship as the stern begins to float, and crushing-strips of soft wood are included in the structure to spread this load.

The actual launch is immediately preceded by removal of the keelblocks and other supports, leaving the vessel standing on the launching cradle. At this time the vessel is restrained by triggers in the ways. At the moment of launch these triggers are released, and the vessel should then start to move. Should no movement occur, hydraulic rams may then be used to overcome the initial resistance. In earlier times screw jacks were sometimes used.

The launch of a vessel, always a poignant moment for the shipyard workers, when an inert mass of steel becomes a floating ship, has long been recognized as an apt moment for naming. The degree of ceremony varies: some ships enter the water watched only by the shipyard workers and staff, while for others a full-dress display is put on, with a distinguished lady guest to press the launching button and to hurl the traditional bottle of champagne across the ship's bow.

On the upper Clyde, the building berths are set at an acute angle to the comparatively narrow river. Even so, the vessel must be prevented from colliding with the opposite bank. This is done by attaching piles of heavy chains to the hull by ropes. The gradually increasing resistance to movement of these masses makes them ideal decelerators. Once stopped, the hull is quickly taken in tow by tugs which then manoeuvre it into a fitting-out basin or alongside a suitable quay.

62 The barque *Amulree* immediately prior to launching at Russell & Co's Kingston yard in 1892. Note that the vessel is being launched fully rigged. The grocer's cart on the left was probably supplying the food for the launch party.

63 *above* The drawing office staff at Clydebank posing under the bow of the battleship HMS *Ramillies*, a Royal Sovereign class battleship. One of the fore-poppets and the drag chains can be seen on the left. Bowler hats distinguished staff and foremen in shipyards. The boys in caps were apprentices.

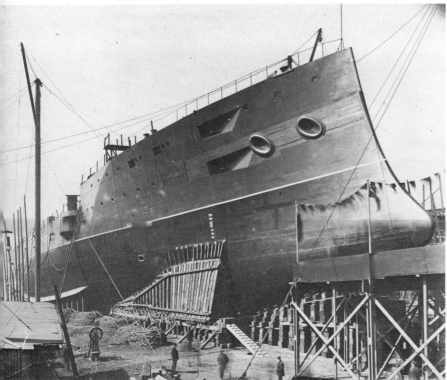

64 *left* The battlecruiser HMAS *Australia* ready for launching at Clydebank in 1911. The very fine hull lines suggest that speed was the prime consideration in the design of this ship and her sisters. The vessel, although financed by the Australian Government, served as a unit of the Royal Navy throughout the First World War.

65 A striking view of the stern of TSS *Princess Margaret*, a Vancouver Sound ferry built for the Canadian Pacific Steamship Company by William Denny and Brothers of Dumbarton. The props on either side of the hull would be removed immediately before the launch.

66 The immense scale of Beardmore's gantry at Dalmuir is indicative of the capital invested in this yard immediately prior to the First World War for building large warships. Here preparations for the launch of HMS *Conqueror* were nearing completion in 1911. This vessel, an Orion class battleship, was the fastest of her class, attaining a speed of 23 knots.

67 The moment of launch of SS *San Salvador* at Clydebank in 1891. The ship is just beginning to slide, and the hydraulic pump and ram used to give the initial push are clearly visible. The vessel was one of a pair built in 1891 for the Brazilian Steam Navigation Company, regular customers of the yard.

68 A launch party at Scotts' Cartsburn shipyard about 1880. The ecumenical gathering of clergymen should have ensured a successful launch, but just in case things went wrong a *lignum vitae* ram and a screw jack were available.

69 The flags of the allies are conspicuous in this view of the launch party for HMS *Ceres* at Clydebank in 1917. The *Ceres* was an Arethusa class light cruiser. Behind the platform is the 'Mighty Hood', not finally completed until after the war.

71 The platform party at the launch of the *Suffolk*, the first of many ships built at Clydebank for the Federal Steam Navigation Company. Note the modest platform and the steam-operated hydraulic pump, a distinct improvement on that shown in plate 67. This ship was built in 1902, and helped to pioneer full-powered steam navigation to Australia.

72 *above* The royal yacht *Alexandra* just after launching from
the Pointhouse yard of A. & J. Inglis by Queen Alexandra in
1907. This vessel was built to supplement the much larger
Victoria and Albert so that royal parties could visit smaller
harbours in the Mediterranean.

73 *below* A launching accident to submarine E35 at Clydebank in 1916. Such incidents were fortunately rare, and the
firm was certainly inexperienced in launching submarines
which, unlike normal ships were launched with their engines
in place.

74 *above* The launching party for the HMS *Pegasus* outside
the main office at Clydebank in 1917. The *Pegasus* was a
seaplane carrier converted from the *Stockholm*, a small railway
steamer ordered prior to the war.

75 *below* The model room at Clydebank laid out for a launch
lunch. Launches were celebrated here until recently.

FITTING OUT

The fitting out of a ship involves the installation, in the bare hull, of all the machinery, equipment, and fittings, necessary to complete it. Some of this work is done on the stocks, but usually much remains to be done after the launch. The main propelling machinery must be installed, including the boilers in a steam vessel, auxiliary machinery, such as condensers, feed and circulating pumps, anchor and mooring winches, cargo-handling equipment, and electric generators (after 1879). Parts of the superstructure, including the funnels, the masts and ventilators were normally fitted after the launch. Navigation equipment on the bridge and the mechanical steering gear had also to be put in place.

The fitting of the passenger accommodation was, however, the field in which the Clyde excelled. Seldom in the van of progressive design, Clyde-built interiors were always well-made, often opulent, and sometimes almost incredibly splendid. The public rooms of the great trans-Atlantic liners offered the most scope to designers, who were often well-known architects. Here the desire to own the most magnificent vessel afloat could outweigh the wish to have the fastest — luxury often outweighed speed in the mind of the first-class trans-Atlantic passenger. Successive heights were reached in the Inman liners *City of Paris* and *City of New York*, the Cunarders *Campania* and *Lucania*, and the later sisters *Mauretania* (Tyne-built) and *Lusitania*. Trans-Atlantic liners did not have a monopoly of luxury: ships built to trade with India and the Far East were also well-appointed, and the first-class cross-channel steamers on the Irish Sea and English Channel could be like miniature liners. Even the relatively mundane Clyde Coast vessels produced some fine saloon interiors.

Backing up the magnificent dining rooms and tea-rooms were well-appointed galleys and bakeries, while other services available to passengers included smokerooms, libraries and gymnasia. For the religious, pipe organs were provided in the *City of Paris* and *City of New York* to accompany the Divine Service.

On a grimmer note, the fitting out of warships was a lengthy business, involving the installation of turrets and their guns, magazines, torpedo tubes, damage control equipment and gunnery control apparatus. Armour plate, too, was frequently installed in the fitting-out basin, large vessels being warped past the heavy crane to complete their plating.

The evolution of shipyard cranes is indeed a fascinating topic. Early engravings show derrick cranes in use in Napier's Govan yard, but this type was not really suited to shipyard work. Other early types included simple rigged posts and sheer-legs, and Stephens had an overhead steam crane on one of their berths for a time. Early in this

76 One set of engines for the Inman liner *City of New York* in the erecting shop of the new engine works at Clydebank. These were the most powerful engines of their day, each set developing 9,200 horse power.

77 A set of triple expansion engines being lifted on board
one of two twin-screw cargo vessels, the *Calvados* or *Trouville*,
built for the London, Brighton and South Coast Railway in
1894. These relatively small engines are typical of many built
by Clydeside shipbuilders and marine engineers.

century lattice-girder posts with jibs pivoted near the top were introduced, precursors
of the post-1914 tower cranes which feature in the conventional idea of a shipyard's
appearance.

78 Hoisting a 12-inch gun-barrel on board HMS *Colossus* at Scotts' Cartsburn yard, Greenock in 1911. Great care had to be taken in installing these large weapons in order to preserve their accuracy.

79 *left* The heavy fitting-out crane at Clydebank lifting one of the 23 double-ended Scotch boilers on to the *Lusitania* in 1905. This heavy crane replaced the sheer-legs seen in plate 100 and was the only one in the yard capable of lifting heavy armour-plate for warships.

80 The upholstery shop at William Denny and Brothers' Yard Dumbarton *c.* 1890. A wide range of furniture is being upholstered. Note the cutting-out table in the foreground.

81 The first-class dining room on board a Greenock-built passenger liner, possibly the *Orinoco* built in 1886 by Cairds for the Royal Mail Steam Packet Company's West India service. Furniture such as this was probably made by a specialist firm.

82 A rare view of steerage accommodation, on the Donaldson liner *Saturnia*, built by Charles Connell & Co in 1910. The largest numbers of emigrants to America and Canada were poor Scots and Irish whose passages were subsidized by the Government.

84　The library of the *City of Paris* (1886) 'with its 900 volumes . . . lined with oak wainscotting with the names of distinguished authors carved on it in scrolls, and its stained glass windows inscribed with quotations from poems referring to the sea'.

83　*left* The influence of Charles Rennie Mackintosh is obvious in this view of the lounge of the TSS *Fuerst Bismark*, built by Fairfield for the Hamburg–American Packet Company in 1905. Note the conventional grand piano painted white on the right.

85　*right* The galley of the TSS *Gelria* of the Koninklijke Hollandsche Lloyd, one of the finest ships built by Alexander Stephen & Sons. Completed in 1912, this view is very reminiscent of a country-house kitchen of the period, apart from the plate racks to prevent breakage during heavy seas.

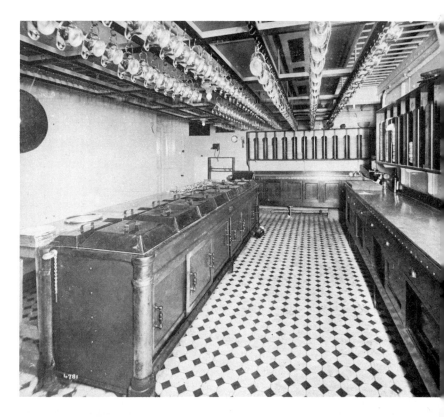

86 The woodworking shop of Scotts'
Cartsburn Yard about 1900. Note the
relative absence of machinery. Here
doors, panelling and other wooden
fittings were made.

89 Victorian taste in evidence in the stained-glass workshops of William Denny and Brothers, Dumbarton, with finished panels and design cartoons in the background, and the designer's table in the centre.

87 *above left* 'To diminish seasickness, you dine in a saloon near the middle of the ship, beautifully decorated with naiads, dolphins, tritons and mermaids, lofty and bright'. Henry Fry's contemporary description of the dining room on board the *City of New York* built at Clydebank in 1886. Note the organ in the balcony.

88 *left* On a more modest scale, the lounge of the PS *Viper*, built by Fairfield for G. & J. Burns' first daylight service from Greenock to Belfast in 1890.

90 The two-berth cabin on board the Indian Government
troopship *Northbrook* built at Clydebank in 1906. Note the
resemblance to a present-day sleeping car.

91 *above right* A second-class four-berth cabin on the
Donaldson liner *Saturnia*, built by Charles Connell & Co in
1910 for the Canadian emigrant traffic. Note the effective use
of space without loss of comfort.

92 *below right* The fitting-out basin at Scotts' Cartsburn Yard
in 1914, with SS *Aspromonte*, an unknown steamer, and the
TSS *Transylvania* built for the Anchor Line's Mediterranean
service, the first Atlantic liner with geared turbines.

93 HMS *Barham*, a Queen Elizabeth
class battleship with three destroyers
in the fitting-out basin at Clydebank
in 1916. In the background is the
150-tons third-generation crane built
by Sir William Arrol & Co. in 1906.

94 *left* The gilded stern decoration on the *City of New York*. By 1900 this type of decoration had disappeared. The beautifully finished flush-riveted hull plating is worthy of note.

95 *below left* An interior view of the submarine E35 built at Clydebank in 1915, illustrating the cramped conditions on these ships, with crew's quarters juxtaposed with machinery.

96 *below* Putting the finishing touches to the Clyde steamer *Queen Alexandra* at Clydebank after a refit. Note the men painting the name on the stern. This vessel was built by William Denny & Brothers for Turbine Steamers Ltd in 1911.

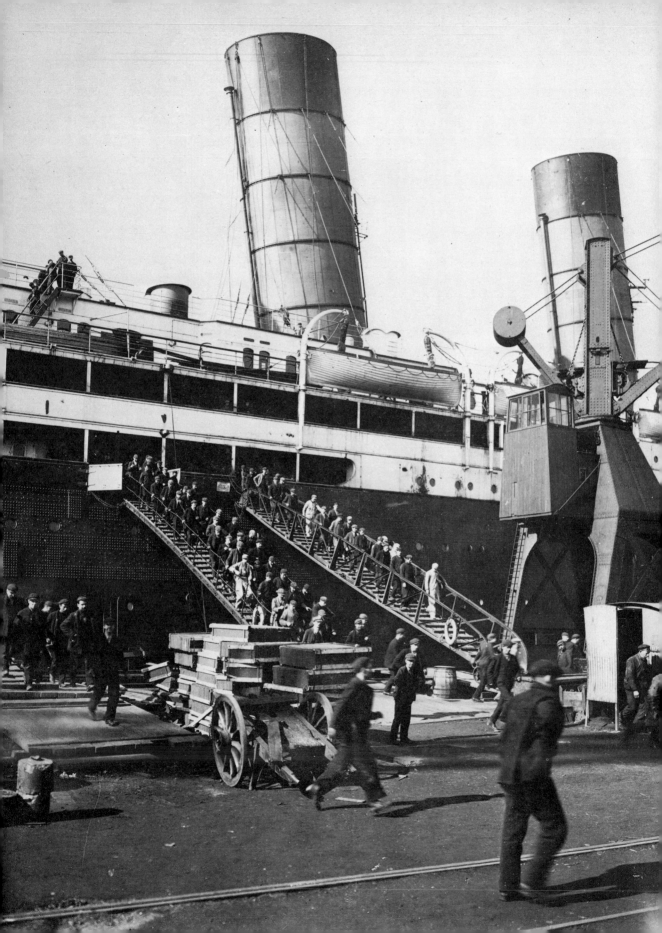

97 *left* Lunch time at Clydebank in 1907, with workmen leaving the nearly complete QTSS *Lusitania*.

98 *right* This rare view of a sailing ship fitting out, at Port Glasgow in 1891, depicts the three-masted barque *Belmont*, built by Russell & Co. for J. G. Hall of Boston, Massachusetts.

99 *below* A Chinese stern-well bucket hopper dredger complete in Lobnitz & Co. Ltd's fitting out basin at Renfrew *c.* 1900. Note the rigger fitting a mast-head halliard.

100 *left* A classic view of Clydebank from the south bank of the river in 1889, with SS *Friesland*, built for the Red Star Line. Note the sheer-legs and, on the extreme left, the giant clock and chimneys of the Singer sewing machine works.

101 *below left* Preparation for war at the Dalmuir fitting-out basin of William Beardmore & Co. Ltd in 1911. On the left is the Russian cruiser *Rurik* and on the right the Dreadnought HMS *Agamemnon*.

102 *below* PS *Mars*, a Clyde paddle steamer of the 'Golden Years', built at Clydebank in 1902 for the Glasgow & South Western Railway. In the background is HMS *Energetic*, a paddle tug.

TRIALS AND DELIVERY

The trials of a ship are held partly to satisfy the builders that all systems are working properly, and partly to demonstrate to the 'owners' that the vessel fulfils the conditions of contract as to speed, reliability and finish. Normally dock trials are held to test the propelling machinery and auxiliaries. The ship then leaves the shipyard, with the workers congregating to bid her farewell. With many of the largest vessels the short voyage down-river attracted numerous spectators.

The ship, with a crew of yard employees, together with representatives of the major subcontractors, and 'owners'' representatives, then proceeds to the formal trials. These consist of speed trials over one of the two measured miles, off Arran and Skelmorlie, endurance and economy trials, and manoeuvring trials. Trial of cargo-handling equipment and anchor windlass must also be made. Sometimes two series of trials – builders' and the acceptance – are held, mainly for very large vessels or for ships with unusual features.

If the trials have been successfully completed, the vessel is formally handed over to representatives of the owners, and the last instalment of the price is paid.

It is not unknown for ships to fail to reach the minimum standards specified in the contract, and it is then open to the 'owners' to reject the vessel. One of the most celebrated cases of rejection was the beautiful Inman liner *City of Rome* built at Barrow in 1884. Owing to a shortage of steel she was built of iron and thus failed to reach the contract speed of 21 knots. Inmans refused to take her, and she was hawked round until eventually chartered by the Anchor Line from the Barrow Steamship Company.

Delivery is sometimes difficult, particularly with small ships for overseas service. In extreme cases it might be necessary to dispatch ships in pieces for erection beside inland lakes, such as Lake Victoria, or, nearer home, Loch Lomond. Vessels such as tugs and dredgers were frequently sent out under their own power, with temporary protection installed, and non-propelling dredgers were towed long distances by ocean going tugs. In the 19th century small steamers might be rigged as sailing vessels for the voyage out to, say, New Zealand.

103   A superb view of the *City of New York* passing Bowling.

104 Steam tug *Vigilant* and steam yacht *Gael* in the fitting-out basin of Lobnitz and Co. Ltd's yard at Renfrew, with the sheer-legs prominent on the right.

LOBNITZ & Cº LTD
RENFREW,
SCOTLAND.
Nº 866.

105 A rare view of dock trials in progress. Here a suction dredger *The Lady Clifford*, built by Lobnitz and Co. Ltd, at Renfrew in 1921 is discharging spoil into the newly completed hopper barge *Dabchick*.

106 Diving party at Clydebank in 1906, preparing to examine the hull of the Cunard liner *Carmania*, prior to sea trials.

107 HMS *Diadem*, a first-class protected cruiser, and the flagship of her class, leaving Fairfield's Govan yard in 1896. Such cruisers were intended for protecting British Imperial interests, and were not a success.

108 A Lobnitz-built steam yacht leaving the Renfrew yard for trials about 1900. Note that sails are rigged. During the Edwardian summers many comparable ships converged on the Clyde to watch the huge sailing yachts race.

109 HMS *Hood*, for a long time the world's biggest vessel, leaving Clydebank in 1920, attended by six Steel and Bennie tugs, and watched by a large group of workmen. This vessel was the largest and finest British battlecruiser.

110 The greatest pre-war Clyde-built passenger liner, the *Aquitania*, about to sail down river from Clydebank in 1914. On the right is the foretop of the battlecruiser HMS *Tiger*. The pastoral scene on the right contrasts with the bustle of activity in the yard.

111 Fairfield elegance at its best – the Canadian Pacific
Steamship Company's *Empress of Russia*, built in 1913,
passing Clydebank on her way to trials. This vessel and her
sister the *Empress of Asia* were the fastest ships on the
Pacific, and were, incidentally, the first cruiser-stern
passenger liners.

114   A trial view of one of the last two of the Clyde water-buses, the *Cluthas*, built by Russell & Co for the Clyde Navigation Trust in 1896. These vessels operated a steamer service between Stockwell Bridge and Whiteinch from 1884 to 1903, when they were replaced by electric trams.

112   *above left* TSS *Gelria*, built by Alexander Stephen and Sons at Linthouse for the Koninklijke Hollandsche Lloyd, on speed trials in 1913.

113   *left* One of a famous trio of cross-channel packets built by Fairfield in 1895 for the Zeeland Steamship Company, the *Prins Hendrik* is seen here on the Skelmorlie measured mile. They achieved a speed of 21 knots.

115 TSS *Orontes* during a lull on trials in the Firth of Clyde. This vessel was built by Fairfield for the Orient Line's Australian Mail trade in 1902, and at that time was the company's largest vessel.

116　A stokehold view of T33 *Hollandia*, built by Alexander
Stephen and Son in 1909 for the Koninklijke Hollandsche
Lloyd, illustrating the deplorable working conditions on a
large coal-fired vessel.

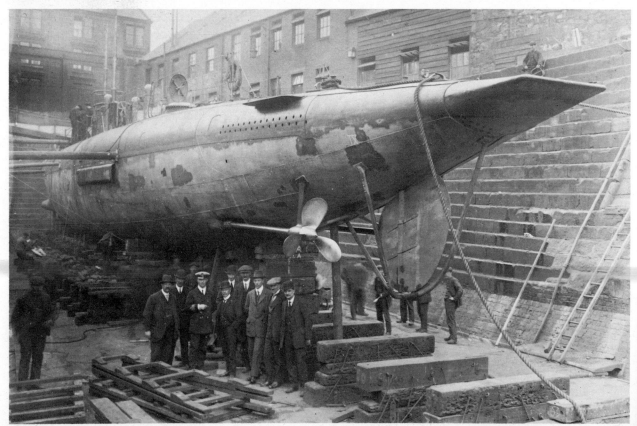

119 The *Warhilda*, a Beardmore-built ship, coming back up river after trials, probably for dry-docking, in 1912. This vessel was built for tropical service, hence the awning supports.

117 *above left* A striking trials view of TSS *Ellora*, a Stephens-built ship for the British India Steam Navigation Company in 1911. The vessel is seen here on the Skelmorlie measured mile, laid out by John Napier on the lands of the Earl of Eglinton in 1866.

118 *left* The submarine *S2*, second to be built in Scotland, undergoing examination in the drydock at the Cartsburn yard of Scotts Shipbuilding and Engineering Company Limited in 1915. This class of submarine, of Italian design, was not adopted by the Royal Navy, and the *S2* was transferred to the Italian Government in the following year.

120 A view of the Govan Graving Docks of the Clyde Navigation Trust, with the Anchor Line *Cameronia*, built by Beardmores in 1921, and the first British passenger liner to be built after the war. The vessel on the left is an Ellerman liner.

121 A most unusual view of SS *Kanieri*, built by Denny at Dumbarton in 1886 for service in New Zealand. Here she is seen temporarily rigged for the voyage out under sail.

122 The four-masted barque *Glenogle*, built by Russell & Co
at Greenock in 1891 for John Edgar & Co. of Liverpool, going
down the Clyde.

SHORT HISTORIES
of the chief builders
with notes on some famous vessels

Barclay, Curle and Co

John Barclay, the founder of the firm, began shipbuilding at Stobcross pool in 1818. His son, Robert Barclay, expanded the business and developed a repair yard, largely to careen and copper the bottoms of American-built clippers. In 1845 the partnership, which gave its name to the company, between Robert Barclay, Robert Curle and James Hamilton, was formed. In 1847 the partners took on John Ferguson as yard manager to develop iron shipbuilding in their yard. The firm continued to grow and, in 1848, launched one of the largest vessels built by that date on the Clyde, the *City of Glasgow*, of 500 tons. In 1855 the company moved to its final home at Whiteinch, enabling the firm to compete for larger orders. Two years later an independent engine works was set up and in 1861 an engine shop built on the site of the old Finnieston Cotton Spinning and Print Works. Further developments of the shipyard at Whiteinch, and the establishment of a new ship-repairing facility there, was delayed, in 1878, by the refusal of the Clyde Trustees to grant permission. The old Stobcross yard had been closed in 1874 when it was purchased by the Trustees for their own purposes. In 1884 the company became limited, later in the century buying a repair works in Whitefield Road, Govan. The firm specialized, from about 1870, in cargo-passenger vessels largely for services to India and second-rate Atlantic services. Although ostensibly a shipyard Barclay Curle's strength has been shared equally by its engine works. In 1894 the engine works moved to the engine shop in Finnieston Street and boiler shop in Kelvinhaugh Street that had previously belonged to Messrs John and James Thomson. The Company took over the North British Engine company at Scotstoun in 1912, a firm that had been set up to build oil engines. Barclay & Curle from then on began to specialize in oil engines, developing, albeit unsuccessfully, the McLaggan diesel. In 1911 the Company built and engined the *Jutlandia*, the first ocean-going motorship to be built in Britain.

OTHER NOTABLE VESSELS

1854 SS *Edina*, a passenger-cargo vessel for the Leith, Hull, Rotterdam, and Hamburg service, employed as a blockade runner during the Crimean and American Civil Wars

1870 The first two steam ships for the Donaldson Line and City Line

1871 The first Ben Line ship

1872 The first two ships for Sir Donald Currie's Castle Line

1879 *Grandtully Castle* for Donald Currie and Company

1892 Steam Yacht *Capercailzie* for Sir John
Burns

1907 *City of Paris* for the City Line

1908 *Monea* for the Peninsular and Oriental
Steamship Company

1911 *Elephanta* for the British India Steam
Navigation Company

John Brown Shipbuilding and Engineering Co, Clydebank

This is perhaps the most well known Clyde yard, largely because the two *Queen Eliza-beths* and the *Queen Mary* were built there. The firm was begun in 1847 as a marine engin-eering business by the brothers James and George Thomson at the Clyde Bank Foundry, Finnieston. The brothers had both worked previously for Robert Napier. In 1851 a shipyard was opened at Cessnock Bank, Govan. The first vessel, the Cunard paddle steamer *Jackal*, was launched in 1852. The firm, from the beginning, specialized in high quality passenger vessels, building the *Jura* for Cunard in 1854, the Company's largest screw steamer, and the Cunard record breaker, *Russia*, in 1867. But it was the move, in 1871, from Cessnock to Clydebank at Dalmuir and the opening of the large modern engine works in 1884, that allowed the firm to become one of the leading British ship-yards. From the 1880s the firm built many very famous vessels, including the *City of Paris* and *City of New York*, in 1888 for the Inman lines and HMS *Ramillies* in 1892. In 1897, as a result of the serious depression of that year, the company was restructured as the Clydebank Shipbuilding and Engineering Company, passing out of the hands of the Thomson family. The new Company did not last long, however, being taken over, in 1899, by John Brown & Company, the Sheffield steelmakers. John Browns at once began a modernization programme, installing new plant and erecting buildings to give the yard facilities to compete for large Admiralty and merchant contracts. It was largely as a result of this modernization, especially the extension and strengthening of the berths and fitting-out basin, that brought the *Lusitania* to Clydebank, instead of to Barrow, as originally intended by Cunard and the Government.

OTHER NOTABLE VESSELS

1851 *Servia* for Cunard, the first trans-Atlantic
liner to cross in under seven days

1890 *Chiyoda*, Japanese cruiser

1904 *Caronia*, last Cunarder with a triple
expansion engine

1910 HMS *Bristol*, first warship fitted with
Brown-Curtis turbines, a modification of

the American Curtis turbines for heavy
duty in warships

1913 *Aquitania* for Cunard

1914 HMS *Barham* launched, HMS *Tiger*
completed

1920 HMS *Hood* completed

Charles Connell & Co

Charles Connell, a manager in the Kelvinhaugh shipyard of Alexander Stephen & Sons, left in 1861 to found the Scotstoun yard. Early products of his firm included a number of distinguished sailing ships such as the tea clipper *Taitsing*. Later the yard specialized in large passenger-cargo vessels, notably the Inman liner *City of Chicago* (1883). The firm built many ships for the Liverpool shipowners T. & J. Harrison.

William Denny and Brothers, Dumbarton

Although the firm of William Denny and Brothers was not established until 1845 the Denny family had long associations with Dumbarton shipbuilding. In 1814 William Denny, the father of the founder, built the *Margery*, the first steamer on the Thames. It was William Denny's sons that formed the company, launching their first vessel the PS *Loch Lomond* in 1845. Unlike some other yards Dennys began as shipbuilders and then became marine engineers, opening their engine works, under the names of Tulloch and Denny, in 1850. Tulloch and Denny built the first compound engines for Cunard, the Austrian Lloyd, and the Peninsulars and Oriental Companies in the 1860s. The firm had some notable firsts; the first steel merchant ship, the *Rotomahana* built for the Union Steamship Company of New Zealand in 1878, and the first turbine passenger steamer, the *King Edward*, in 1901. The firm specialized in railway steamers and passenger ferries. It possessed the first commercial test tank in the world, built, in 1883, with advice from R. E. Froude, son of William Froude, the constructor of the first test tank in Torquay in 1872.

OTHER NOTABLE VESSELS

1845 PS *Dumbarton Youth*, the first ship to be built for the Blue Funnel Line

1851 PS *British Queen* for McIver and Company

1890 *Scot* for the Union Steamship Company

1901 *Shamrock* II for Sir Thomas Lipton, an America's Cup challenger

1908 *Otaki* for the New Zealand Shipping Company, the first merchant ship to be fitted with combined reciprocating and turbine machinery, the exhaust steam from the low pressure cylinder being used to drive a turbine. The ship was sunk in 1917 after an heroic engagement with the German commerce raider *Moewe*.

1913 *Paris*, a channel ferry for the Newhaven-Dieppe service, the fastest vessel for her size then afloat

The Fairfield Shipbuilding and Engineering Co

In 1852 John Elder joined the partnership of the mill-wrighting business of Randolph, Elliot and Company of Centre Street, Glasgow, the firm becoming Randolph, Elder and Company. From then on the firm specialized in marine engines and boilers, in 1860 building their first ships at a small yard formerly the property of James R. Napier. From the outset the firm was at the forefront of developments in marine technology. In 1854 compound engines invented by Elder were successfully applied to the ship *Brandon*, reducing the rate of coal consumed per indicated horse power from $4\frac{1}{2}$-lbs. to $3\frac{1}{4}$-lbs. By experimenting with Watt's proposal for steam jacketing the cylinders Elder was able to further reduce coal consumption to between 2-lbs. and $2\frac{1}{2}$-lbs. Success was immediate: by 1868, when the original partnership was broken up and Elder became sole partner of the firm now known as John Elder and Company, 111 sets of engines had been built.

In 1864 the Fairfield shipyard was laid out, the first vessels to be built being four blockade runners for the Confederacy. In 1868 Elder decided to concentrate the whole of the firm's production at Fairfield, building new engine and boiler works there, not completed until 1874. The output of the yard during Elder's brief proprietorship until his death in 1869 was a prodigious 30 ships. The following year a new partnership was formed headed by Sir William Pearce, previously general manager at Robert Napier's yard. Under his control the firm became, perhaps, the most important in Western Europe, building some of the fastest and most technically advanced ships of the time. Between 1878 and 1885, Pearce designed and built a series of 'greyhounds of the Atlantic' that successfully held the Blue Riband, including the *Arizona* (1879), *Alaska* (1881), and *Oregon* (1883) for the Guion Line and the *Umbria* and *Etruria* (1884/5) for Cunard. At the same time the development of the more efficient triple expansion engine enabled the firm to penetrate new markets, especially on the longer routes to India, South Africa and the Antipodes, building the *Kinfauns Castle* for the Castle Line in 1879 and the *Ormuz* for the Orient Line in 1886. Nor was the firm's only success in long haul passenger ships, but also in cross-channel fast packet steamers. In 1886 the London, Chatham and Dover Railway had the *Victoria* built by the firm, 'making the round trip once per day for a month, taking not more than one hour on any run between Dover and Calais'. From 1875 to 1889 the average speed of Fairfield-built cross-channel packets was pushed up from 13.5 to 19 knots.

In 1885 Sir William Pearce had reconstructed the company, renaming it the Fairfield Shipbuilding and Engineering Company. Three years later he died, to be succeeded by his son Sir William G. Pearce, who was chairman until his death in 1907, when the firm passed under the control of a consortium. In 1893 the firm reached its zenith in the Atlantic market, building the *Campania* and *Lucania* for Cunard. Thereafter the size of berths at Fairfield prevented the firm from competing for the larger Cunarders built at

Clydebank. The firm now specialized in long haul quality passenger vessels for Canadian and South African services, building a succession of ships for the Canadian Pacific Railway Company and for the Castle Line, including the Empresses of Russia and Asia in 1911. In 1907 the firm built the *Heliopolis* and *Cairo*, two pioneer ships for the Egyptian Mail Steamship Company's service between Marseilles and Alexandria.

Moreover the yard had a special relationship with the Admiralty, building the first compound engines for a navel ship, HMS *Constance*, in 1865, and building HMS *Nelson* in 1876. In 1885 the firm built 11 stern wheeler 'Crocus' class gun boats for the Egyptian campaign in six weeks. From 1897 until the outbreak of the First World War the firm built about 40 naval ships including HMS *Argonaut* (1878), HMS *Good Hope* (1892), HMS *Indomitable* (1907) and HMS *New Zealand* (1911).

OTHER NOTABLE VESSELS

1880 *Livadia*, Yacht for the Tsar of Russia

1889 *Calais-Douvres* A cross-channel steamer with a speed of 20 knots. She made the crossing between Calais and Dover, frequently in less than an hour.

1890 *Dunnottar Castle* for Sir Donald Currie's Castle Line. On her maiden voyage she reached the Cape of Good Hope in just under 17 days, a world record.

1894 *Giralda*, Steam yacht for Colonel McCalmont, later the Spanish Royal Yacht.

1905 *Empress of Britain* for the Canadian Pacific Steamship Company.

A & J Inglis

In 1840/1 Anthony Inglis expanded his business of bellhanger, smith and gas fitter in Anderston to include shipsmithing and machine making. By 1847 Anthony had been joined in partnership by his brother John, a marine engineer, and together they set up as engineers and boilermakers, at the Whitehall Foundry, Anderston. The firm built in 1850 the engines for the tug *Clyde*, which are now preserved on the riverside at Renfrew. During the 1850s the firm's reputation for marine engines grew, especially after the construction in 1855 of the engines for the *Tasmanian*, one of the largest and fastest ships of the time. In common with other engineering firms A. & J. Inglis opened a shipyard of their own in 1862 at Pointhouse. One of the first vessels built at the new yard was the *Erl King*, the first ship to steam to Shanghai via the Cape of Good Hope. Prior to 1914, 53 ships were built for the British India Steam Navigation Company. Although the yard built a variety of vessels from oil tankers to private yachts, it was in the latter that the firm displayed excellence, building the Royal Yacht *Alexandra* for King Edward VII in 1907, the *Safa-el-Bar* for the Khedive of Egypt in 1894, and the *Adriana* for Henry Bubb in 1888. The yard was sold to Harland and Wolff in 1919.

135

1869 *Norman Court* a clipper for the bankers Baring Brothers. In six out of seven years from 1870 she made better time from China than the *Cutty Sark*.

1879 *Cosmos* the first Clyde-built ship to be fitted with electric light.

1890 *William Mackinnon* for Sir William Mackinnon's East Africa Company, built in sections and carried overland from Zanzibar to Lake Nyasa, the ship was fitted with a hose 'for spraying boiling water on the war-like natives'.

Lithgows

In 1874 a partnership headed by Joseph Russell and including Anderson Rodger and William T. Lithgow took over the bankrupt Bay yard of Messrs McFadyen at Port Glasgow. In the late 1870s there was no economically viable alternative to sail for merchant ships used on the long routes to South America and the Pacific. From the outset Russell and Co. set out to supply vessels for these trades. The partners decided that rather than build clippers, which, although fast, were expensive to run and had small carrying capacity, they would design and build slower, more capacious and more easily maintained vessels, often incorporating all the latest labour saving devices. In 1879 such was the firm's success that the partners leased another yard at the east end of Greenock specifically to build this class of ship. Three years later the partners puchased the Kingston yard at Port Glasgow, which was to become the largest on the lower Clyde. During this period William Lithgow decided that to improve the financial structure of the company, charges (that sum of money added to the contract price to pay for drawings, yard maintenance etc.) and costs would have to be reduced. His solution was the novel idea of building ships to two standard specifications. These vessels were built on 'spec' and if a buyer could not be found William Lithgow floated a company to manage them himself. This helps to explain why the yard headed the Clyde list for production in the years between 1882 and 1892, when 271 ships were built. In 1891 the original partnership was dissolved, Russell retiring, Lithgow becoming sole partner and Anderson Rodger taking over the Bay yard on his own account. By the 1890s the firm was ceasing to build sailing ships and beginning to build steam tramp ships. The policy of building standard ships was maintained. In 1908 William Lithgow died, leaving over a million pounds, and the yard was taken over by his able sons James and Henry Lithgow, both of whom had served their time in the yard. The brothers bought the Bay yard from Anderson Rodger's successors in 1912 and the yard of Robert Duncan and Company in 1915. The name of the firm was not changed to Lithgows Ltd until 1918.

OTHER NOTABLE VESSELS

1878 *Falls of Clyde*, still afloat, preserved in Honolulu

1882 *Falls of Dee* for Wright and Graham, Glasgow, made a record passage in 1909 from New South Wales to Chile

1890 *Hinemoa*, a refrigerated ship which
      equalled some of the best times of the
      clippers.

1891 *Maria Rickmers* the largest sailing ship in
      the world at the time.

1905 *River Clyde*, converted into a troop landing
      craft for the Gallipoli campaign.

Lobnitz & Co

In 1847, before William Simons & Co moved to Renfrew, James Henderson & Son began building ships there. The firm later became Henderson & Coulburn, and began specialising in dredgers, some of which were supplied to Ferdinand de Lesseps, both for the construction of the Suez Canal and for his abortive attempt to build a Panama canal. In 1895 the company was reorganized as Lobnitz & Co Ltd, and became world famous for dredgers of various types, hopper barges and rock-breakers.

Robert Napier and Sons

Robert Napier was the father of shipbuilding on the upper Clyde; from his works came many of the men who were to found the principal yards on the river. In 1821 he leased his cousin David Napier's engine works at Camlachie. In 1823 he produced his first successful marine engine for the PS *Leven*, which is now preserved in the new shopping precinct at Dumbarton. In 1827 two vessels fitted with Napier's engines, the *Clarence* and *Helensburgh*, came first and second in a race for steam yachts organized by the Northern Yacht Club, a measure of his initial success as a marine engineer. By 1830 he was able to re-equip the Vulcan Foundry in Washington Street, Glasgow, as a marine engine works. In 1835 he built his first ocean-going engines for the *Berenice* for the East India Company, and in 1838 his first trans-Atlantic engines for the *British Queen*. In 1840 he began his long relationship with the British and North American Royal Mail Company, later Cunard, engining and supervising the building of the first four ships. In 1841 he decided to establish an iron shipyard at Govan, launching his first ship in 1843. Robert Napier retired from the business in 1860, leaving the firm in the hands of his two sons and two relations. By the 1870s, however, the yard had run down and only Robert's son, John Napier, remained of the four partners. On Robert's death in 1876 the business was sold and bought by a consortium headed by A. C. Kirk, one of Napier's apprentices and designer of the first large marine triple expansion engine, built by John Elder and Company for the *Propontis* in 1873. In 1886 Kirk built the *Aberdeen* at Govan, fitted with a new

137

design of triple expansion engine, which was so successful commercially that many owners and builders were encouraged to adopt it. After the death of Kirk in 1892, the firm was bought in 1900 by William Beardmore and Sons of Parkhead Forge. The shipyard and engine works were moved to new premises at Dalmuir, a little down river from John Brown's yard at Clydebank. The Dalmuir yard was fitted as one of the most modern yards on the Clyde, equipped to build battleships and other capital Admiralty vessels.

OTHER NOTABLE VESSELS

1855 *Persia*, first iron mail ship for Cunard

1861 *China*, first screw-driven mail ship for Cunard

1861 *Black Prince* for the Admiralty, sister ship of the *Warrior*, the first iron battleship

1865 *Pereire* and *Ville de Paris* for the Compagnie Générale Transatlantique, Blue Riband holders

Scotts Shipbuilding and Engineering Co

In 1711 John Scott began building small fishing and coastal craft at Greenock; a trade which was carried on by successive generations of the family throughout the 18th century. As the century progressed craft became larger and the firm began to penetrate new markets. In the 1790s the building by the firm of the *Brunswick*, of 600 tons, and *Caledonia*, of 650 tons, marked the turning point towards the construction of large ocean-going vessels. From then the firm specialized in building vessels for both the West and East India trade, which culminated in the building of the famous East-Indiaman *Lord of the Isles* in 1853. This ship in 1856 beat two of the fastest American clippers in a race from Foo-chow-foo to London, delivering her cargo 'without one spot of damage'. There were close links between Scotts and the family of James Watt, resulting in the firm's quick adoption of steam propulsion. By 1816 Scotts had built two of the earliest Clyde steamers, the *Active* and *Despatch*, and also the *Shannon*, for the service between Limerick and Kilrush: between 1819 and 1821 Scotts built the largest steamships in Britain: in 1819, the *Waterloo* of over 200 tons, in 1820, the *Superb* of 240 tons, and in 1821, the *Majestic*, of 345 tons. Although the *Superb* was built for the Glasgow-Liverpool trade, she became, in 1824, one of the first steamers to trade in the Mediterranean. The engines for these early steamships were built either by David Napier or James Cook in Glasgow; but in 1825 the firm bought its own engine works in Greenock, building their first engines for the Mediterranean steamer *Trincania*. By 1829 the engine works was building 'the largest engine ever made', and the yard was described as 'the most complete in Britain, excepting those of the crown'. From then until the 1860s Scotts' reputation for steamship building was only challenged by the Napiers. Scotts' market was not for main line Atlantic vessels, but rather for ships for the longer routes to Egypt, India, South Africa and the West

Indies. In 1839 the firm built the *India* for the company newly formed by Sir John Ross to trade with India via the Cape of Good Hope, and also the *Dee*, the first ship to be built for the Royal West India Mail Company. In 1865/6 Scotts built the first three iron steamers, the *Agamemnon, Ajax* and *Achilles* for the Holt line, some of the first long distance ships with compound engines. From then until 1914 the firm continued to build similar vessels, on average one a year, for Holt and the China Navigation Company.

The yard's association with the Admiralty is longer than any other on the Clyde. In 1803 they built their first naval ship, the *Prince of Wales*, and in 1849 the first steam frigate, the *Greenock*, to be built on the Clyde. From the late 1830s to the 1890s the majority of the Admiralty work carried out by the firm was in the development of satisfactory high pressure water tube boilers for naval ships. The results of this work were incorporated in two ships, the *Thrush* and *Sparrow*, built in 1888/9. From then until the outbreak of the First World War the firm became increasingly involved in Admiralty work, engining the battleships *Barfleur* in 1894, *Canopus* in 1900, and *Prince of Wales* in 1902, and the Dreadnought *St Vincent*, in 1910 and building the Dreadnoughts *Colossus* in 1909 and *Ajax* in 1912. In 1912 the 'S1' the first submarine to be built in Scotland, was ordered from the firm, being followed by a series of further orders.

OTHER NOTABLE VESSELS

1819 *Robert Bruce*, the first steamer to trade between the Clyde and Liverpool

1836 *Jupiter*, for the Clyde-Dublin service, established a record, making the journey in 16 hours six minutes

1839 *Tagus*, first ship for the Peninsular and Oriental Company

1858 *Thetis*, an experimental vessel designed to test high pressure boilers, providing initial pressures of 115 psi for compound engines

1876 *Hinemoa*, New Zealand Parliamentary Yacht

1911 *Hildebrand*, largest vessel in the Booth line fleet

1913 *Transylvania*, for the Anchor Line, at that time the largest vessel to have been built on the lower Clyde, and the first Atlantic liner with geared turbines

1916 HMS *Swordfish*, the first British steam submarine

William Simons and Co

In 1810 William Simons began shipbuilding at Greenock; but in 1812 he moved to the Isle Aux Noix, near Montreal, in Canada. Here the firm built mostly naval craft for the war, with the United States of America, of 1814. In 1818 the firm returned to Greenock, continuing to build sailing vessels until 1826, when their first steamer, the *Fingal* was built for a Belfast company. In 1826 the firm moved to Whiteinch and shortly afterwards, in 1860, to their final home, the London Works, Renfrew. With the construction of four self-propelling hopper barges for the Clyde Trustees between 1861 and 1863, the firm began its long association with dredger building. From 1866 to 1872 the firm built eleven bucket ladder dredgers and nine stationary and propelling dredgers. In 1872 the firm combined the bucket ladder dredger and hopper barge to produce the first hopper dredger, the *Canada*. Between 1860 and 1910 the firm built over 200 dredgers, improving their original design by introducing the stern well dredger, and the suction dredger in 1889.

OTHER NOTABLE VESSELS

1851 *William Connal*, the first ship fitted with wire rigging

1861 PS *Rothesay Castle* for the Glasgow-Rothesay passenger service. On the outbreak of the American Civil War she was converted into a notable blockade runner

1868 *India* for the Anchor Line, the first trans-Atlantic liner to be fitted with four-cylinder compound engines

1889 *Beaver* for the Natal Government, the first hopper suction dredger built

1890 *Finnieston* for the Clyde Trustees, the first elevating deck ferry steamer

1892 *Foyers* for the Indian Government, the first clay-cutter suction dredger built in Britain

Alexander Stephen and Sons

In 1750 Alexander Stephen began building ships at Burghead, eight miles from Lossie-mouth on the Moray Firth. Alexander's nephew William followed him into the business, serving ten years at Burghead before setting up his own yard at Footdee, Aberdeen, in 1793. William's son, another William, also set up his own yard at Arbroath in 1814. In 1828 both the Aberdeen and Arbroath businesses foundered and were taken over by the elder William's son Alexander and from then on the firm was known as Alexander Stephen and Sons. In 1830 the Aberdeen yard was closed and in 1843 Alexander moved the centre of his production to Dundee. In 1850 the firm built the *Amazon* of 800 tons, the largest ship built on the river to date. Early in 1851 Alexander moved to Kelvinhaugh on the Clyde, leaving his son William in charge at Dundee. The Clyde yard was set up as an iron shipyard, building its first steamship, the *William McCormick*, in 1854. In October 1861 Alexander Stephen, the son of the founder of the Kelvinhaugh yard, won approval from the Admiralty and Lloyds to build composite ships with 'bones of iron and skin of wood'. In 1869 the firm moved to its final home at Linthouse. Up to this time the firm had largely specialized in sailing vessels; building the occasional steamship with engines bought in from outside. In 1871 an engine works was built at Linthouse. From then on the firm specialized in cargo-passenger vessels of the type similar to those built by Barclay Curle. In 1878/1879 Stephens built the first four such ships for the Clan

Line. By 1886 the firm had built 193 ships on the Clyde, 12 more than their nearest rival Barclay Curle. In 1904 the Allan liner *Virginia* was built at Linthouse, one of the earliest turbine Atlantic steamers. In 1901 the *Port Morant* was built, the first of a succession of banana boats. In 1905 the *Nicaya* was built, the first banana boat for the newly established firm of Elder and Fyffes. From the turn of the century until the First World War orders were mostly for cargo-passenger vessels, coming largely from Elder-Dempster, Lord Furness's companies and the Cayzer-Irvine companies.

OTHER NOTABLE VESSELS

1863 *Sea King*, a fully rigged auxiliary screw steamer, renamed the *Shenandoah*, the most celebrated Confederate commerce raider

1865 *Zeta* for Henry Bath and Sons of Swansea, 'the first ordinary trading ship to navigate the Straits of Magellan'.

1867 *Abeona*, fastest clipper in the Allan Line's North Atlantic fleet

Yarrow and Co

Yarrows was established at Poplar on the Thames in 1865 by Alfred Yarrow. At first the firm specialized in steam launches and river steamers; but it was a small step from building these vessels to torpedo and gun boats. In 1871 Yarrow became interested in torpedo boats; he built his first experimental boat, equipped with a spar-torpedo, in 1872. By 1877 Yarrow's reputation for such craft was well established. With the introduction of the self-propelled torpedo by Whitehead in that year, naval strategists came to realise the significance of the torpedo boat as an offensive weapon. Yarrow was quick to take advantage of this opportunity, building vessels for many of the world's navies. In 1892 Yarrow with the assistance of Lord Fisher, than at the Admiralty, built the *Havock* and *Hornet*, the first destroyers, designed to chase and destroy the fast French torpedo boats then building. In 1906 the firm decided to move from Poplar to Scotstoun on the Clyde, largely because wage rates on the Thames were high and steel was not available locally. The first ship to be built at Scotstoun, the *Para* for Brazil, was launched in 1908. In 1911 HMS *Lurcher* was built, the first British destroyer to have a guaranteed minimum speed of 32 knots.

BIBLIOGRAPHY

Among the many sources consulted during the compilation of this volume, the following have proved particularly useful.

MANUSCRIPT

Graham J. Kennison, 'Robert Napier, 1791-1876, Father of Clyde Shipbuilding?', unpublished dissertation for the degree of B.A. in Economic History, University of Strathclyde, 1973

George Blake, 'History of William Simon and Co', unpublished manuscript kindly loaned by Mr T. R. Evans

H. Brown, 'History of Clydebank Shipyard, 1847-1953', unpublished manuscript kindly loaned by his widow.

PRINTED

General

Elijah Baker III, *Introduction to Steel Shipbuilding*, 2nd Edition, McGraw Hill, London 1953.

James Dolby, *The Steel Navy*, Macdonald, London 1962

C. L. Duckworth & G. E. Langmuir, *Railway and Other Steamers*, Shipping Histories Limited, Glasgow 1948

Henry Fry, *The History of North Atlantic Steam Navigation*, Sampson Low Marston & Co., London 1896

C. R. Vernon Gibbs, *Passenger Liners of the Western Ocean*, Staples Press, London 1952 and *Passenger Liners of the Five Oceans,* Putnam, London 1963

F. T. Jane, *Fighting Ships*, Sampson Low Marston & Co., London 1914

Chief Engineer King, U.S.N., *The War-Ships of Europe*, Griffin & Company, Portsmouth 1878

T. D. Manning, *The British Destroyer*, Putnam, London 1961

K. T. Rowland, *Steam at Sea: a History of Steam Navigation*, David & Charles, Newton Abbot 1970

John Shields, *Clyde Built*, William MacLellan, Glasgow 1949

John Mayer *et al. Some of the Leading Industries of Glasgow and the Clyde Valley*, Blackie and Son, Glasgow 1876

Relating to particular yards

Development of Shipbuilding on the Upper Reaches of the Clyde and Souvenir of Mr James Gilchrist's Jubilee with Messrs. Barclay, Curle and Company Limited, 1911

Ships and Shipbuilding, Barclay, Curle and Company Limited, 1818-1932, 1932

Denny's Dumbarton – Souvenir, 1908

Denny Dumbarton, 1844–1932

The Building of the Ship, being an historical and descriptive narrative of the works of the Fairfield Shipbuilding and Engineering Company Limited, London 1891

The Fairfield Shipbuilding and Engineering Works : History of the Company; Review of its Production; and Description of the Works, London 1909

Two Centuries of Shipbuilding by the Scotts at Greenock, third edn. 1950

William Simons and Company, A Century of Shipbuilding, 1810–1910

William Simons and Co. Ltd., an illustrated catalogue with notes c. 1926

John L. Carvel, *Stephen of Linthouse, A Record of Two Hundred Years of Shipbuilding*, 1950

Half a Century of Shipbuilding, Mercantile and Naval, with a description of the Clydebank Works of James and George Thomson, London 1896

Alastair Borthwick, *Yarrows – The First Hundred Years*, 1965

J. M. Reid, *James Lithgow, Master of Work*, Hutchinson, 1964